COMBINATION CHALLENGE !

by

Lou Hays and USCF Senior Master John Hall

HAYS PUBLISHING   DALLAS, TEXAS

Copyright © Lou Hays, 1991

PRINTED IN THE UNITED STATES OF AMERICA

Editor: Lou Hays
Book Design and Typeset: Lou Hays
Chess Consultant: John Hall
Research Assistant: Douglas Stidham
Proofreaders: John Hall, Mike Richards, Bob Mapes, Al Sprague, Will Brugge

Diagrams electronically created on "Diagram 2.0."

Hays Publishing
P.O. Box 797623
Dallas, Texas 75379

ISBN 1-880673-86-X Softcover

to Susan,

*A truly wonderful wife
who understands that
chess takes time.*

A WORD FROM THE PUBLISHER

During a recent visit to New York City, I stopped in as a spectator at a large chess event and interviewed a number of chessplayers about the types of chess books they felt would be needed during the 1990's. The idea was suggested to me that a comprehensive diagram training book in **algebraic notation** was definitely missing in the marketplace. This was reconfirmed to me by players of every level. As a result of these thought-provoking conversations this book was created.

Achieving the Master or Expert class in chess requires great tactical awareness. The very foundation for becoming a strong chessplayer is the ability **to recognize and take advantage of tactical situations** when they occur in your games. No amount of opening, strategic or endgame study can overcome a lack of combinational skill. Period. The training system in this book is strongly recommended for all players below the 2200 level as an aid in developing tactical proficiency. Masters may use the book to keep their skills sharp.

It is my sincere hope that this book will be helpful to all chessplayers in developing and maintaining a high level of tactical accuracy. The algebraic format should prove a most comfortable working environment for everybody.

Lou Hays

Dallas
July 1991

RAPID CHESS IMPROVEMENT THROUGH TACTICS TRAINING

COMBINATION CHALLENGE! is both an instrument of learning and of entertainment. If you simply love reading and solving chess problems you will always keep this book handy. The sheer volume of diagrams should keep you entertained for years to come. If your game is lacking tactically, nothing will be more beneficial to you now than devouring as many of these diagrams as possible for the next few months. For those players who are seriously trying to improve and learn to play sharp, tactical chess the following is recommended:

A) TRY TO SPEND <u>SOME</u> TIME EVERY DAY WORKING ON THE DIAGRAMS. At the rate of 20 diagrams per day you can go through the book in around 2 months; 15 per day will take just under three months; 10 per day around four months.

B) SOLVE DIRECTLY FROM THE BOOK, NOT ON YOUR CHESSBOARD. This is slightly more difficult, but will help your visualization ability. Use your board and pieces only on the more difficult diagrams.

C) DO NOT SPEND MORE THAN 5 MINUTES AT A TIME ON ANY ONE DIAGRAM. Some of these solutions are long and challenging, others short and easy. If you have no idea of the solution to a diagram after 5 minutes, it is better to look it up and get the right idea into your head instead of becoming frustrated and wasting valuable time. The concept is to see as many diagrams and solutions as you can in the shortest period of time possible, not force yourself to endure a gruesome exam every day. Diagram training is learning by repetition, a sort of "osmosis." You will, after examining enough positions, begin to develop a "feel" for tactics. Do not worry about how much you are or aren't learning as you go. Just continue a steady diet of diagrams and you will rapidly begin to see and use these patterns in your own games. A significant rise in strengh and rating should follow.

D) ENJOY YOURSELF. Take a firm but relaxed attitude toward learning to play tactically. Enjoy the diagrams. They will definitely help you become a strong player. Chess is a long term proposition and long term fun. View it as such.

EXPLANATION OF SYMBOLS

1.   WHITE TO PLAY AND WIN

1...   BLACK TO PLAY AND WIN

!   STRONG MOVE

!!   VERY STRONG MOVE

?   WEAK MOVE

??   BLUNDER

+   CHECK

+-+   DOUBLE CHECK

CHECKMATE

e.p.   CAPTURES EN PASSANT

x   CAPTURES

TABLE OF CONTENTS

1. BACK RANK

Combinations based on the vulnerable back rank are made possible by the targeted King being hemmed in by his own pawns and/or pieces. The simplest examples of this type of combination occur when the back rank is left without a Queen or Rook to help defend against invading heavy pieces. As some of these examples will show, even an apparently well-guarded back rank can often be exploited by the resourceful attacker.

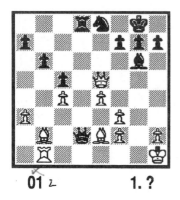

01   1. ?

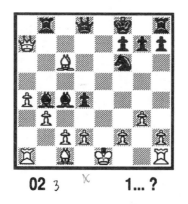

02   1... ?

03   1... ?

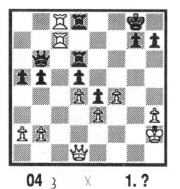

04   1. ?

05   1... ?

06   1... ?

07   1. ?

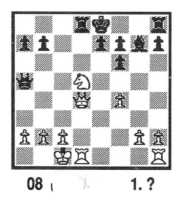

08   1. ?

09   1... ?

BACK RANK

10 ⎪ ✗ 1... ?

11 ⎪ ✓ 1... ?

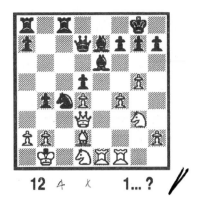

12 4 ✗ 1... ? ⁄

Erreur ...Dd5+

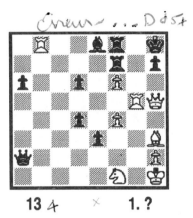

13 4 ✗ 1. ?

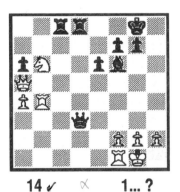

14 ✓ ✗ 1... ?

15 ✓ ✗ 1... ?

16 ✓ ✗ 1... ?

17 ✓ ✗ 1... ?

18 ✗ 1... ?

BACK RANK

3

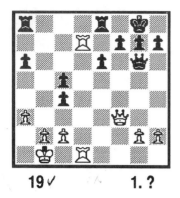

19 ✓   1. ?

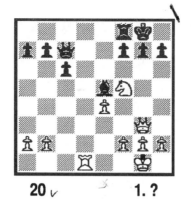

20 ✓   1. ?

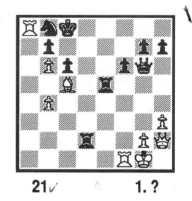

21 ✓   1. ?

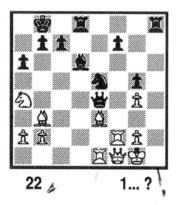

22   1... ?

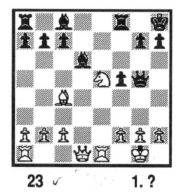

23 ✓   1. ?

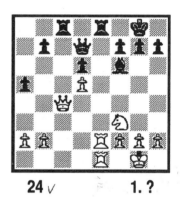

24 ✓   1. ?

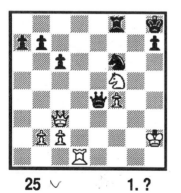

25 ✓   1. ?

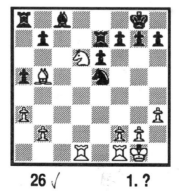

26 ✓   1. ?

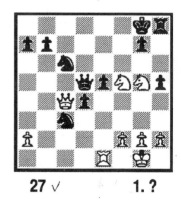

27 ✓   1. ?

BACK RANK

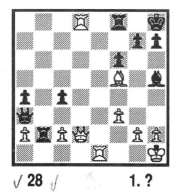

√ 28 √   1. ?

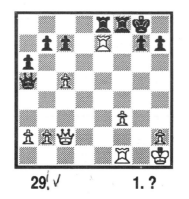

29 √   1. ?

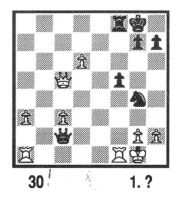

30   1. ?

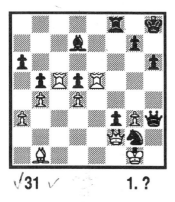

√ 31 √   1. ?

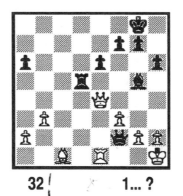

32   1... ?

33 √   1. ?

34   1. ?

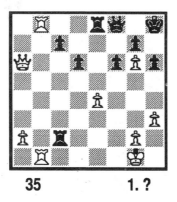

35   1. ?

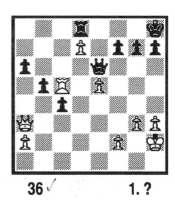

36 √   1. ?

BACK RANK

37 ✓   1... ?

38 ✓   1... ?

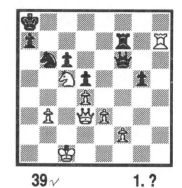

39 ✓   1. ?

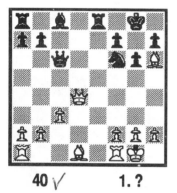

40 ✓   1. ?

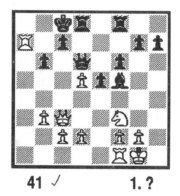

41 ✓   1. ?

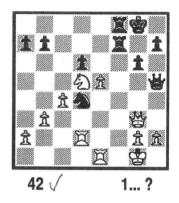

42 ✓   1... ?

43 ✓   1... ?

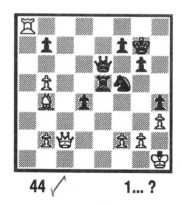

44 ✓   1... ?

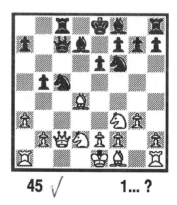

45 ✓   1... ?

BACK RANK

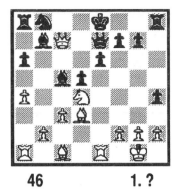

46   1. ?

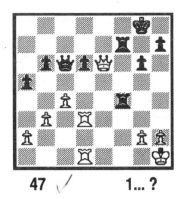

47 ✓   1... ?

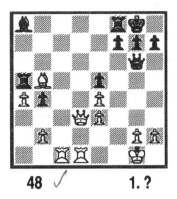

48 ✓   1. ?

49   1... ?

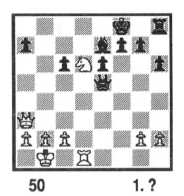

50   1. ?

51   1... ?

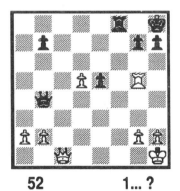

52   1... ?

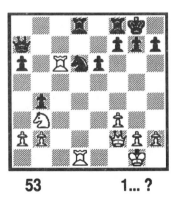

53   1... ?

54   1... ?

BACK RANK

55   1... ?

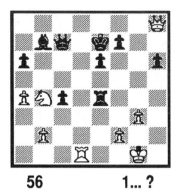

56   1... ?

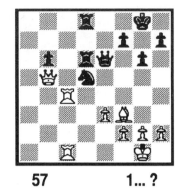

57   1... ?

58   1... ?

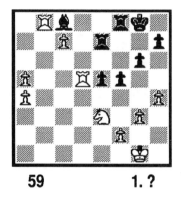

59   1. ?

BACK RANK

1) 1.Rd1! Qxe2 2.Qxg7+! Nxg7 3.Rxd8+ Ne8 4.Rxe8#.

2) 1...Qe8+! 2.Bxe8 Rxe8+ 3.Kd1 Be2+ 4.Ke1 Bg4 + 5.Kf1 Bh3+ 6.Kg1 Re1#.

3) 1...Rxd6! 2.Qxd6 [2.exd6 Qe1+ and wins] **2...Rd8** and wins. If 3.Qxe7 then 3...Rd1#.

4) 1.Qg4 g6 2.Qe6+! Kh8 3.Qf6+! wins since 3...Rxf6 allows 4.Rxd8+ and mate next.

5) 1...Qxg2+! 2.Rxg2 Rb1+ 3.Rg1 R [either] xg1#.

6) 1...Qd4+ 2.Kh1 Qf2! and wins, since 3.Rxf2 allows 3...Re1+ and mate next, while if 3.Qb5, then 3...Re1 wins.

7) 1.Qxc7+! Rxc7 2.Rxd8+ Rc8 3.R [either] xc8#.

8) 1.Qa4+! Qxa4 2.Nxc7+ Kf8 3.Rxd8+ Qe8 4.Rxe8#.

9) 1...Nc5! 2.Rxe8+ [2.Qg3 Rxe1+ 3.Qxe1 Rd1 and wins] **2...Qxe8 3.Qf3** [3.Qe3 Rd1+ 4.Kf2 Ne4+ and if 5.Ke2, then 5...Bg4+, while if 5.Kf3, then 5...Nd2+ 6.Kf2 Rf1+ 7.Ke2 Re1+! wins White's Queen] **3...Bg4!** winning, since 4.Qxg4 allows Qe1#.

10) 1...Rc5! and now if 2.Rxc5 then 2...Qxb7. If instead 2.dxc5, then 2.Qd1#.

11) 1...Bxe4! and if 2.Qxe4, then 2...Qf1+ mating, while if 2.Rxe4, then again Qf1+ mates.

12) 1...Bf5! Nxf5 [If 2.Qxf5, then 2...Qxf5 3.Nxf5 Nxd2+ 4.Ka1 Rc1#] **2...Qxf5! 3.Qxf5 Nxd2+ 4.Ka1 Rc1+ 5.Qb1 Rxb1#.**

13) 1.Rxe8! Rxe8 2.Rg7 Rxg7 3.Qxe8+ Rg8 4.f7 and wins. ~ _ _ ◻ d 5+

14) 1...Rc1! 2.Rxc1 Qd1+! 3. Rxd1 Rxd1#.

15) 1...Rxc2! 2.Rxc2 Rxc2 3.Qd1 [if 3.Qxc2 then Qe1#]3 ...Qxa2 and Black is winning.

16) 1...Bh6! 2.Re1 [if 2.Bxh6 then 2...Qf2+ 3.Kh1 Qf1+ mating] **2...Bxe3+ 3.Qxe3 Rf1+! 4.Rxf1 Qxe3+** and wins.

17) 1...f3+! 2.Kg1 Qxf1+! 3.Kxf1 Rd1#.

18) 1...b5! 2.Qxc6 Qf1+ 3.Rxf1 Rxf1#.

19) 1.Qxa8! Rxa8 2.Rd8+ Rxd8 3.Rxd8#.

20) 1.Nh6+! Kh8 2.Qxe5! Qxe5 3.Nxf7+! Kg8 [if 3...Rxf7, then 4.Rd8+ mating] **4.Nxe5** and White has won a piece.

21) 1.Rxb8+! Kxb8 2.Qxe5+! and if 2...fxe5, then 3.Rf8+ mates.

22) 1...Rh1+! 2.Kxh1 Qh7+ 3.Kg1 Qh2+!! 4.Kxh2 Nf3+-+ 5.Kh1 Rh8#.

23) 1.Qxd6! cxd6 2.Nf7+ Kg8 [if 2...Rxf7 then 3.Re8+ mates] **3.Nxg5** and wins.

24) 1.Qc7! Qb5 [if 1...Rxc7 or 1...Qxc7, then 2.Rxe8+ forces mate] **2.a4!! Qxa4 3.Re4! Qb5** [if 3...Rxe4, then 4.Qxc8+ mates, or if 3...Rxc7, then 4.Rxe8+ is mate. Also if 3...Qxe4, then 4.Rxe4 wins, since 4...Rxc7 loses to 5.Rxe8#] **4.Qxb7!** and Black resigned since 4...Qxb7 allows 5.Rxe8+ and mate next.

25) 1.Qxf6+ Rxf6 2.Rd8+ Rf8 3.Rxf8#.

26) 1.Nf5! Rd7 [if 1...exf5, 2.Rd8+ mates next] **2.Bxd7** and wins material.

27) 1.Rxe5! Nxe5 [if 1...Qxc4, then 2.Re8#] **2.Qc8+ Qd8 3.Qxd8#.**

28) 1.Qc3! Qc5 [if 1...Qxc3, then 2.Rxf8 is mate] **2.Rxf8+ Qxf8 3.Qxb2** and wins.

29) 1.Qb3+ Kh8 2.Qf7! wins, since 2...Rxf7 allows 3.Rxe8 and mate next.

30) 1.Qc4+ Kh8 [if 1...Rf7, then 2.d7 Qd2 3.Rad1 and wins] **2.Qxg4!** and wins, since 2...fxg4 allows 3.Rxf8#.

31) 1.Qxf3! Rxf3 2.Rc8+! Bxc8 3.Re8+ Rf8 4.Rxf8#.

32) 1...Bh4! 2.Rg1 [2.g3 Bxg3 3.hxg3 Rh5+] **2...Qxg1+ 3.Kxg1 Rd1+** mates.

33) 1.Be6!! fxe6 [if 1...Rxd3, then 2.Qe8#, or if 1...Bxe6, then 2.Qc8+ Rd8 3.Rxd8+ mates next] **2.Qc8+ Bd8 3.Qxd8+! Rxd8 4.Rxd8+** and mate next.

34) 1.Qxb4 axb4 2.Rxa8+ Be8 3.Bxd5! and if 3...Qxd5, then 4.Rxe8#.

35) 1.Rxe8 Qxe8 2.Qa4! and wins, as 2...Qxa4 allows 3.Rb8+ forcing mate.

36) 1.Rc8! Rxc8 [if 1...Qxd7, then 2.Qf8+!] **2.Qe7!! h6** [if 2...Qxe7, then 3.dxc8=Q+ and mate next] **3.Qxe6 fxe6 4.dxc8=Q+** wins.

37) 1...Qg2+! 2.Qxg2 Rxe1+ 3.Qf1 Rxf1#.

38) 1...Qb2! 2.Qd1 [if 2.Rxb2, then 2...Rxa1+ is mate in two, while 2. Rxa2 allows mate after 2...Qxb1+] **2...Qxf2+ Kh1 3. Qxg2#.**

39) 1.Qg6! Rf8 [if 1...Qxg6, then 2.Rh8+ mates in three] **2.Qxf6 Rxf6 3.Rh8+** and mate in two.

40) 1.Ba4! b5 2.Bxb5 Qxb5 3.Qxf6 Qe5 4.Rae1! Qxf6 5.Rxe8#.

41) 1.Qc6! [threatening 2.Ra8#] **1...Qxc6 2.dxc6 Kb8 3.Rfa1** and mate by 4.Ra8 cannot be stopped.

42) 1...Qe2!! and if 2.Rdxe2 Nxe2+ 3.Rxe2 Rf1#, or if 2.Nf6+ Rxf6 3.exf6 Qxd2 wins a piece.

43) 1...Rxa3!! and wins, since 2.Qxa3 allows mate after 2...Qe1+ and 2.Rxa3 again fails against 2...Qe1+. Finally, if 2.bxa3, then 2...Qxa1+ 3.Qb1 [or 3.Rb1] and 3...Re1+ mates.

44) 1...Re1+! 2.Bxe1 Qxe1+ 3.Kh2 Ng3! 4.Ra1 Nf1+! and wins, since 4.Kg1 (or h1) is followed by 5...Qxa1.

45) 1...Nd3+ 2.Qxd3 Qc1+ 3.Rxc1 Rxc1#.

46) 1.Nxe6! fxe6 2.Bg6+ Kf8 3.Rxe6! winning, as 3...Qxc7 allows 4.Re8#, and 3...Qxe6 allows mate after 4.Qd8+.

47) 1...Qe4!! and White resigns as the Black Queen is diverted from pinning the Rook on f7.

48) 1.Rc8! Rxc8 2.Qd8+ Rxd8 3.Rxd8#.

49) 1...Rgc8! and White Resigns. The Rook on c1 cannot be defended, and if it moves along the first rank, there comes ...Qxa1!! winning.

50) 1.Nf5! c5 [1...exf5 2.Rd8#, or if 1...Bxa3 2.Rd8#] **2.Qxa7** and wins, as 2...exf5 loses to 3.Qa8+.

51) 1...Ng4! 2.Qxd6 1.Rf1#.

52) 1...Qd2! attacking both Queen and Rook, and 2.Qxd2 allows 2...Rf1#.

53) 1...Ne4! 2.fxe4 Rxd1#, or if 2.Qxa7, Rxd1#.

54) 1...Qe4! and if 2.Qe2, then 2...Qxe2 3.Rxe2 Rxd1+ and mate next or if 2.Qxe4 then 2...Rxd1+ mates.

55) 1...Qxe4! and if 2.Qxd6, then 2...Qe1#, while 2.dxe4 allows 2...Rd1+ and mate next.

56) 1...Qd6! 2.Rxd6 Re1+ 3.Kh2 Rh1#.

57) 1...Nxe3! 2.Re4 [if 2.fxe3 Qxe3+ 3.Kf1 Rd2 4.Qc5 Rf2+ 5.Kg1 Rxf3+. wins. Also if 3.Kh1 Rd1+ mates] **2...Qxe4! 3.Qe2** [if 3.Bxe4, then 3...Rd1+] **3...Qxf3! 4.gxf3 Rd1+ 5.Rxd1 Rxd1+ 6.Qxd1 Nxd1** and Black wins a piece.

58) 1...Qb2! 2.Rd3 [if 2.Qd3 Qa1+! wins, but not 2...Rxd3 allowing 3.Rc8+ mating. Also if 2.Qxb2 Rd1#] **2...Qb1+** and wins.

59) 1.Rxc8! Rxc8 2.Rd8+ Re8 3.Rxe8 Rxe8 4.Nd5! Rc8 [4...Kf7 5.Nb6 and 6.c8=Q] **5.Ne7+** wins.

2. THE PIN

Pinning is one of the most frequently occurring tactical motifs. The pin involves an attack on an enemy piece which is situated on a straight line (i.e. a file, a rank, or a diagonal) and in front of a more valuable piece. Since the first attacked piece is less valuable, it dare not move because the more valuable piece behind it would be exposed to immediate attack. Hence the first piece "in line" is pinned down and, reluctantly, subject to capture.

There are two kinds of pins, the absolute and the relative pin. An absolute pin involves a piece in front of its King, which cannot legally move away to protect itself since this would leave the King in check. For this reason the absolute pin is normally very damaging. The relative pin is one without the King's involvement. In some of these cases the pinned piece may be able to move away if it can in turn produce a stronger threat of its own. For this reason relative pins must be examined with some degree of caution.

60 3 √   1. ?

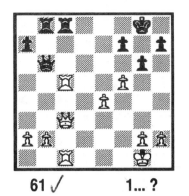

61 √   1... ?

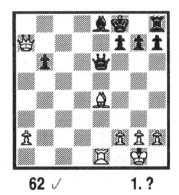

62 √   1. ?

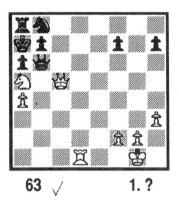

63 √   1. ?

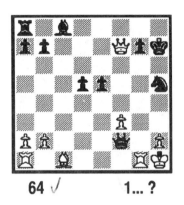

64 √   1... ?

65 √   1. ?

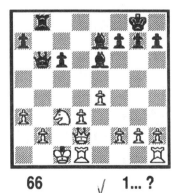

66   √ 1... ?

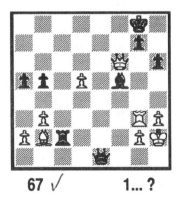

67 √   1... ?

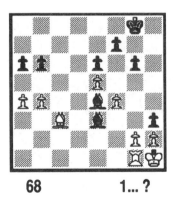

68   1... ?

THE PIN

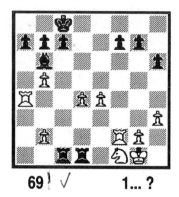

69 ✓   1... ?

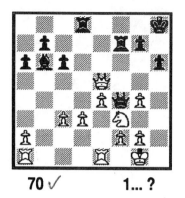

70 ✓   1... ?

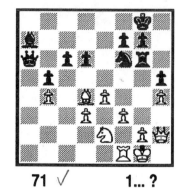

71 ✓   1... ?

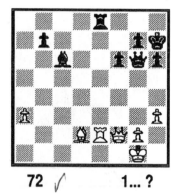

72 ✓   1... ?

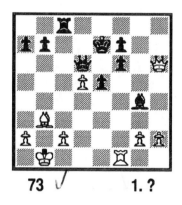

73 ✓   1. ?

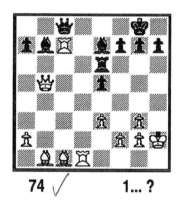

74 ✓   1... ?

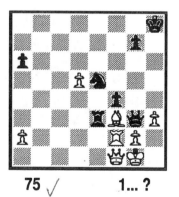

75 ✓   1... ?

76 ✓   1... ?

77 ✓   1. ?

THE PIN

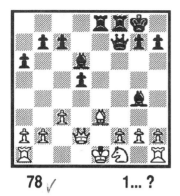 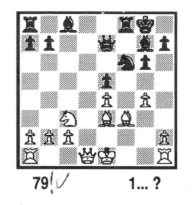 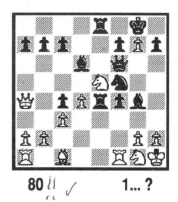

78 ✓   1... ?   79 ✓   1... ?   80 ✓   1... ?

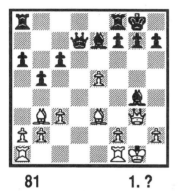 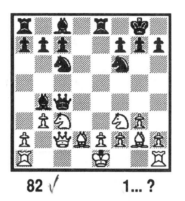 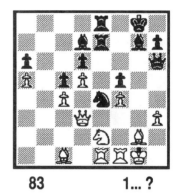

81   1. ?   82 ✓   1... ?   83   1... ?

 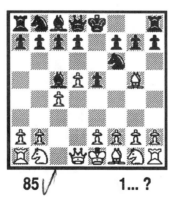 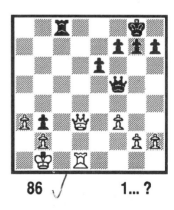

84   1... ?   85 ✓   1... ?   86 ✓   1... ?

THE PIN

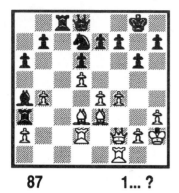 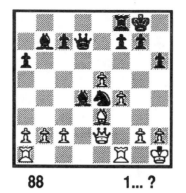 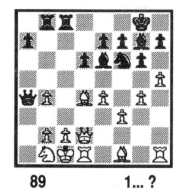

87   1... ?   88   1... ?   89   1... ?

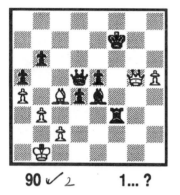 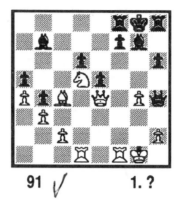 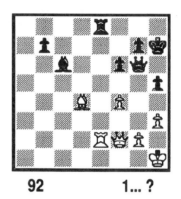

90 ✓2   1... ?   91 ✓   1. ?   92   1... ?

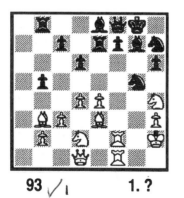 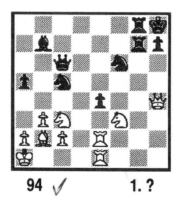 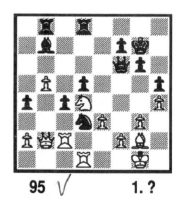

93 ✓1   1. ?   94 ✓   1. ?   95 ✓   1. ?

THE PIN

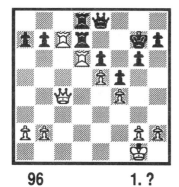

96   1. ?

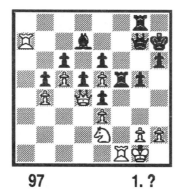

97   1. ?

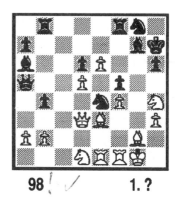

98   1. ?

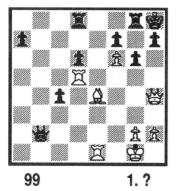

99   1. ?

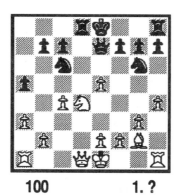

100   1. ?

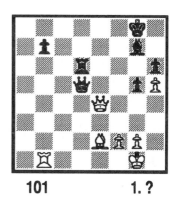

101   1. ?

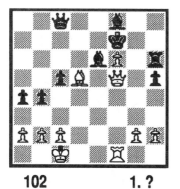

102   1. ?

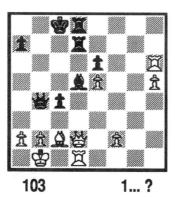

103   1... ?

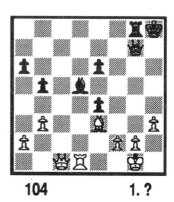

104   1. ?

THE PIN

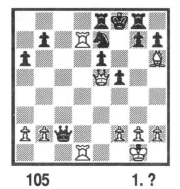

105   1. ?

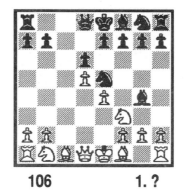

106   1. ?

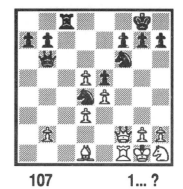

107   1... ?

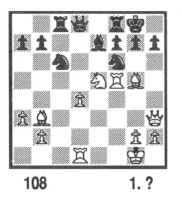

108   1. ?

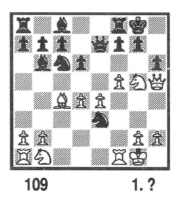

109   1. ?

110   1. ?

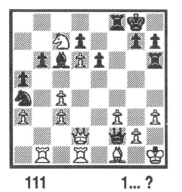

111   1... ?

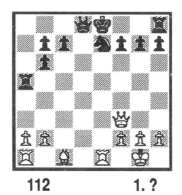

112   1. ?

113   1. ?

THE PIN

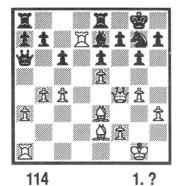

114   1. ?

115   1... ?

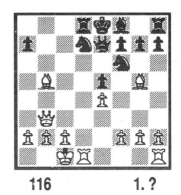

116   1. ?

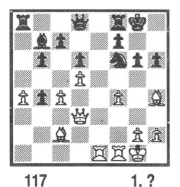

117   1. ?

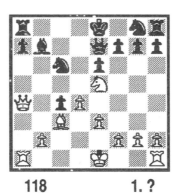

118   1. ?

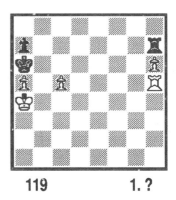

119   1. ?

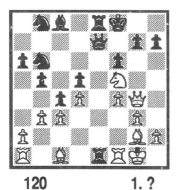

120   1. ?

121   1. ?

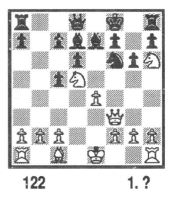

122   1. ?

THE PIN

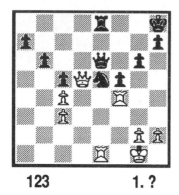

123   1. ?

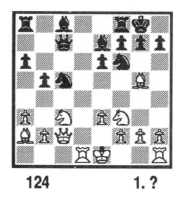

124   1. ?

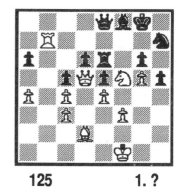

125   1. ?

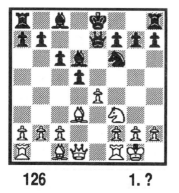

126   1. ?

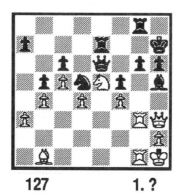

127   1. ?

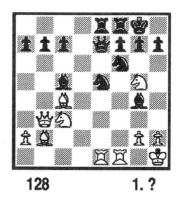

128   1. ?

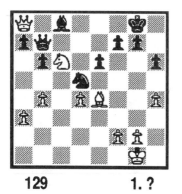

129   1. ?

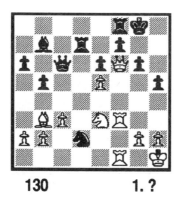

130   1. ?

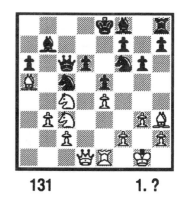

131   1. ?

THE PIN

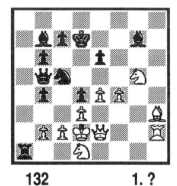

132   1. ?

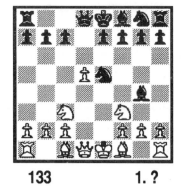

133   1. ?

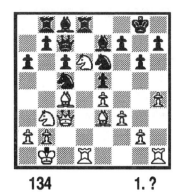

134   1. ?

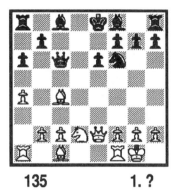

135   1. ?

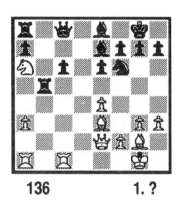

136   1. ?

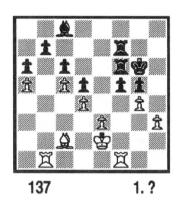

137   1. ?

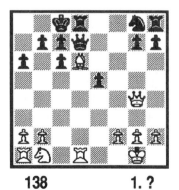

138   1. ?

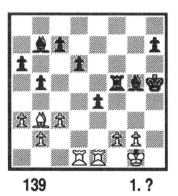

139   1. ?

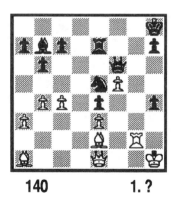

140   1. ?

THE PIN

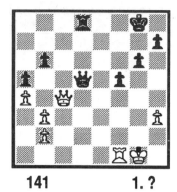

141   1. ?

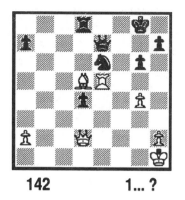

142   1... ?

143   1. ?

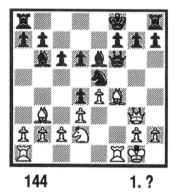

144   1. ?

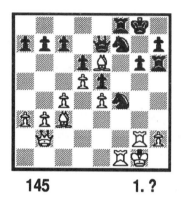

145   1. ?

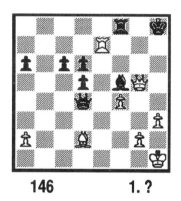

146   1. ?

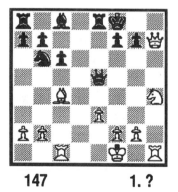

147   1. ?

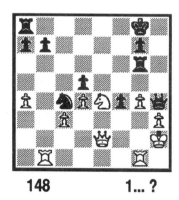

148   1... ?

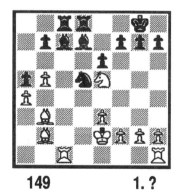

149   1. ?

THE PIN

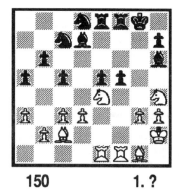

150   1. ?

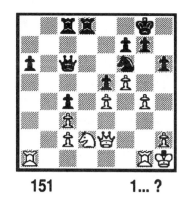

151   1... ?

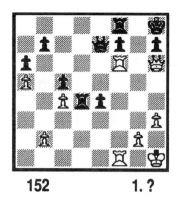

152   1. ?

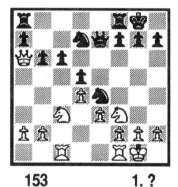

153   1. ?

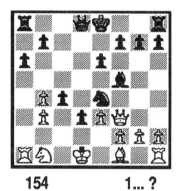

154   1... ?

155   1. ?

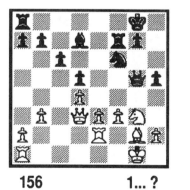

156   1... ?

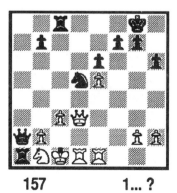

157   1... ?

158   1. ?

THE PIN

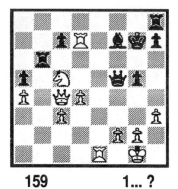

159   1... ?

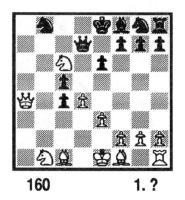

160   1. ?

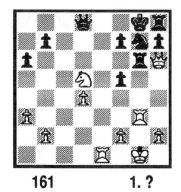

161   1. ?

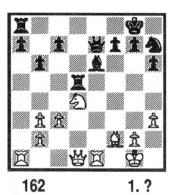

162   1. ?

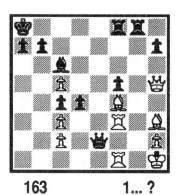

163   1... ?

164   1. ?

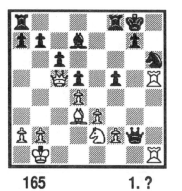

165   1. ?

166   1. ?

167   1. ?

THE PIN

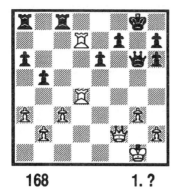

168   1. ?

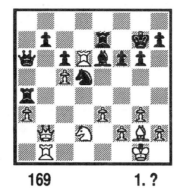

169   1. ?

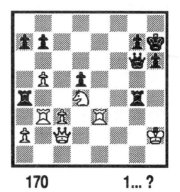

170   1... ?

171   1. ?

THE PIN

60) 1.Nxh7! Kxh7 2. Rh5+ Kg7 [2...Kg8 3.Qg6+ and wins] **3.Be5+ f6 4.Rg5!** and White wins.

61) 1...Rxc5 2.Qc5 Rc8! and if 3.Qxb6, Rxc1+ followed by 4.axb6 winning a whole Rook.

62) 1.Qa3+ Qe7 [if 1...Kg8, 2.Bxh7+ wins the Black Queen] **2.Bc6!!** and if 2...Qxa3 3.Re8#.

63) 1.Rb1! and Black Resigns, for if 1...Qxc5 2.Rxb7#.

64) 1...Bg4!! [threatening 2...Bxf3+] and White resigned. If 2.Rxg4 Qf1+ 3.Rg1 Ng3+! 4.hxg3 4.Qh3#.

65) 1.Ne6! fxe6 [if 1...Ne8 or 1...Nh5, then 2.Qf8+ followed by Ng5#. Obviously 1...Nxe6 is met by 2.Qxd2] **2.Rxg6+ Kf7 3.Rg7+** and mate to follow.

66) 1...Bg5! 2.f4 Bxf4! and White Resigns, as 3.Qxf4 is met with 3...Qxb2#.

67) 1...Qxg3! 2. Kxg3 gxf6 White resigns.

68) 1...Kh7! [A remarkable King march which forces mate due to the powerful pin of the Be4] **2.Be1** [nothing else makes any difference] **2...Kh6 3.Bc3 Kh5 4.Be1 Kg4 5.Bc3 hxg2+ 6.Rxg2+ Kh3 7.Be1 Bxg2#.**

69) 1...Rxd4! [even stronger than 1...Bxd4] **2.Rxd4 Bxd4 3.g3 Rc2** winning the Rook.

70) 1...Bxf2+! 2.Kf1 [on 2.Kxf2, Qxe5 wins the Queen since the Nf3 is pinned] **2...Bxe1** and wins.

71) 1...Bxd4+ 2.Nxd4 Qb6! 3.Qxd6 Nxe4 4.Qd7 [or 4.Qe5 Re6! and the Queen must give up its protection of the Nd4] **4...Nd6!** winning the Nd4.

72) **1...Bxg2! 2.Rxe8** [or 2.Qxg2 Rxe2] **2...Bc6+!** winning an important pawn.

73) **1.Qh4! Bd7 2.Rxf6! Qxf6 3.d6+** and wins the Queen.

74) **1...Rh6+! 2.Kg1 Rh1+! 3.Kxh1 Qh3+ 4.Kg1 Qxg2#.**

75) **1...Re1! 2.Qxe1 Nxf3+ 3.Rxf3 Qxe1+.**

76) **1...Nf3+! 2.Qxf3** [2.Kh1 Nxe1! 3.Qxe7 Rf1#] **2...Qxe1+! 3.Rxe1 Rxf3** winning the exchange.

77) **1.Bh7+ Kxh7 2.g8=Q+! Kxg8 3.Qxh2.**

78) **1...d4!! 2.cxd4** [on 2.Qxd4 Black has 2...Qxf2#] **2...Bb4! 3.Qxb4 Qxf2 #.**

79) **1...Nxg4! 2.Qe2** [on 2.Bxg4 Black has 2...Qxh4+ and 3...Bxg4] **2...Qh4+ 3.Bf2** [after 3.Kd1 Nxe3+ 4.Qxe3 Rxf3! wins, as 5.Qxf3 allows 5...Bxg4] **3...Nxf2 4.Qxf2 Qxf2+ 5.Kxf2 Bg4** winning the Bf3.

80) **1...R(e8)xe5! 2.dxe5 Qh4** [threat: 3...Ng3#] **3.Bxf4 Rxf4! 4.Ne2 Bxe2 5.Rxf4 Ng3+! 6.Kg1 Bc5+ 7.Rf2 Qf4 8.hxg3 Bxf2+ 9.Kh2 Qh6#.**

81) **1.e6! Bxe6 2.Bd4! f6** [2..g6 3.Qe5 wins] **3.Qg4!** wins, since 3...Kf7 is followed by 4.Re1! piling up on the Be6.

82) **1...Rxe2+! 2.Kd1** [2.Nxe2 drops the Queen] **2...Rxd2+! 3.Kxd2 Ne4+** and wins.

83) **1...Nc3** wins since 2.Nxc3 Rxe1 wins the exchange, while 2.Bf3 allows 2...Qxh3.

84) **1...Qf5! 2.Nc3 Rfe8 3.Re1 Rxe4! 4.Nxe4 Re8 5.g4 Rxe4!** winning, as 6.gxf5 allows 6...Rxe1#.

85) 1...Ne4! [the "relative" pin is broken] 2.Be3 [after 2.Bxd8 Black has 2...Bxf2#] 2...Bxe3 3.fxe3 Qh4+ 4.g3 Nxg3 winning easily.

86) 1...Rd8! 2.Qxf5 Rxd1#.

87) 1...Rcc3! 2.Qe2 Bb5! 3.Rfd1 [after 3.Bxb5 Rxe3 wins] 3...Qc7! 4.Bd4 Rxd3! 5.Rxd3 Qc4! winning material.

88) 1...Ng3+! 2.hxg3 Qh3+ 3.Kg1 Bxe3+ 4.Rf2 [or 4.Qxe3 Qxg2#] 4...Qxg2#.

89) 1...Bh6! 2.g5 Bxg5! 3.f4 Bxf4 4.Be3 Bxe3 5.Qxe3 Qxc2#.

90) 1...Rxb3+!! 2.Bxb3 Qxb3+ and wins.

91) 1.Qg6! [threatening 2.Nf6+] 1...Bxd5 [If 1...fxg6, then 2.Nf6#] 2.Bxd5 Qe7 3.Rxf7 Rxf7 3.Rf1 wins.

92.) 1...Qxg2+! 2.Qxg2 Rxe2 wins the exchange.

93) 1.Ng6! and wins the Black Queen.

94) 1.Nxe4! Ncxe4 2.Rxe4 Nxe4 3.Rxe4! Qxe4 4.Ng5!! Qg6 [on 4...Qxh4 5.Nf7 is mate] 5.Qxh7+!! [a spectacular blow] 5...Qxh7 6.Nf7#.

95) 1.Rxd3!! cxd3 2.Ne6+! fxe6 3.Rc7+ and wins Black's Queen.

96) 1.Rdxd7 Rxd7 2.Qb5! wins.

97) 1.Rxf5 exf5 2.e6! Qxd4 3.Nxd4 wins a piece.

98) 1.Qxe4!! fxe4 2.Bxe4+ Kh8 3.Ng6+ Kh7 4.Nxf8+-+ Kh8 5.Ng6+ Kh7 6.Ne5+! Kh8 7.Nf7#.

30

99) 1.Qxh7+! Kxh7 2.Rh5#.

100) 1. Bxc6+! bxc6 2.Nxc6!! Rxd1+ 3.Rxd1 Qd7 [if 3...Qe6 or 3...Qc5 then 4.Rd8#] **4.Rxd7 Kxd7 5.Nxa5** winning since White is several pawns ahead.

101) 1.Bc4!

102) 1.Re1! Rxf6 [on 1...Bxd5 2.Qxc8 wins] **2.Bxe6+ Qxe6 3.Qh7+ Bg7 4.Qxh5+ and Rxe6.**

103) 1...Be4! 2.Qxb4 Rxd1#.

104) 1.Bd4 Qxd4 [1...e5 2.Bxe5] **2.Qh6#.**

105) 1.Qf6#.

106) 1.Nxe5!! Qa5+ [on 1...Bxd1 White plays 2.Bb5+ Qd7 3.Bxd7+ Kd8 4.Nxf7+ Kxd7 5.Kxd1] **2.Bd2 Bxd1 3.Bxa5** winning. 3...dxe5 allows 4.Bb5#.

107) 1...Rc2! 2.Bxc2 [or 2.Qe3 Ne2+ 3.Kf2 Ng4+ winning] **2...Ne2#.**

108) 1.Bxf6! Bxf6 [or 1...gxf6 2.Qg4+, Kh8 3.Nxf7+ winning the exchange] **2.Qxh7+!!** [the proverbial bolt from the blue!] **2...Kxh7 3.Rh5+ Kg8 4.Ng6!** and 5.Rh8# cannot be prevented.

109) 1.f6! Bg4 [if 1...gxf6 then 2.Qg6+ Kh8 3.Qh7#] **2.Qg6!** and mate next.

110) 1.Nc5! dxc5 2.Bf4! [far superior to 2.Rxd7 Rxd7 3.Ra8 Qxa8 4.Qxa8+ Rd8 and Black can still resist] **2...Bd6** [on 2...Qxf4 3.Qc8+ Ke7 4.Qxb7 wins] **3.Bxd6 Rb6 4.Qxd7+!** and wins since 4...Kxd7 allows 5.Bxb8+.

111) 1...Rxf3 2.Qxf2 Rfxh3+ 3.Kg1 Rh1#.

112) 1.Bg5! Rxg5 [after 1...f6 White wins with 2.Rad1 Qc8 3.Bxf6! gxf6 4.Qxf6 threatening 5.Qxe7#] **2.Rad1 Qc8 3.Qe3! 0-0 4.Qxg5** winning the exchange.

113) 1.Qf4 Ne6 2.Qa4+ Qc6 3.Bb5 and wins.

114) 1.Bc5! Kf8 2.Qf6! winning the Bishop since 2...Bxc5 allows 3.Qxf7#.

115) 1...Rxc4 2.Rxc4 Ne4! 3.Qc2 [if 3.Rc1, then 3...Nd6 still wins the exchange] **3...Bxc4 4.Qxc4 Nd2** and 5...Nxf1.

116) 1.Rxd7! Rxd7 2.Rd1 Qe6 3.Bxd7+ Nxd7 4.Qb8+! Nxb8 5.Rd8#.

117) 1.Re6! fxe6 2.Qxg6+ Kh8 3.Bxf6+ and **Qh7#.**

118) 1.d5! exd5 2.Nxc6 Qd7 3.Na5! Qxa4 4.Rxa4 and the double threats 5.Nxb7 and 5.Bxg7 win.

119) 1.c6! Rxh6! [a nice try... now if 2.Rxh6 it's stalemate] **2.c7! Rc6 3.Rh6 Rxh6 4.c8=B#.**

120) 1.Ba3! [of course 1.Nxe7 wins but the text is much quicker] **1...Bxf5** [1...Qxa3 2.Qxg7#] **2.Bxe7+** winning.

121) 1.f6! [threatening 2.Qh7#] **1...hxg5 2.Qg6!** and wins.

122) 1.e5! dxe5 2.Nxe7 Kxe7 3.Bg5 Bf5 4.Nxf5+ gxf5 5.Qxf5 Qd6 6.Rd1 Qe6 7.Bxf6+ Qxf6 8.Rd7+ winning.

123) 1.Kf1! [avoiding 1...Nf3+] **1...Kg7 2.Rf2! Kf6 3. Rfe2 h5 4.Rxe5.**

124) 1.Bb1! [threatening 2.Bxf6 and 3.Qxh7#] **1...g6 2.Bxf6 Bxf6 3.Ne4 Be7 4.b4!** wins the Nc5.

125) 1.Ne7+! Kf7 [1...Bxe7 2.Qxe6+] **2.Nc6+ Kg8 3.Nd8! Qxd8 4.Qxe6+ Kh8 5.Qf7** wins.

126) 1.e5 Bxe5 2.Nxe5 Qxe5 3.Re1 Ne4 4.f3 winning the Knight.

127) 1.Nxg6!! Bxg6 2.Rxg6! Rxg6 3.Bxf5 Nxf4 4.Rxg6! Qxg6 [if 4...Nxh3, then 5.Rxe6+ Kh8 6.Rxe7 and wins] **5.Bxg6+ Kxg6 6.Qg4+** winning.

128) 1.Bxf7+!! Rxf7 2.Rxe5! Qxe5 3.Qxf7+ Kh8 4.Nce4! Qxb2 [or 4...Bd4 5.Bxd4 Qxd4 6.Qxe8+! Nxe8 7.Rf8#] **5.Nxf6 Qe2 6.Qg8+! Rxg8 7.Nf7#.**

129) 1.Ne7+! Qxe7 2.Qxc8+ Qf8 3.Bh7+! wins the Queen.

130) 1.Bxe6 Nxf3 [1...Qxe6 2.Qxe6 fxe6 3.Rxf8+] **2.Qxg6+ Kh8 3.Qxh5+ Kg7** [3...Kg8 4.Bxd7 Qxd7 5.gxf3 and 6.Rg1+ decides] **4.Nf5+ Kg8 5.Qg4+** and 6.Qg7#.

131) 1.Nxe5! dxe5 2.Qxd8#.

132) 1.Nxe6! Nxe6 2.Qg4! Qc6 3.Qxg7+

133) 1. Nxe5!! Bxd1 2.Bb5+ c6 3.dxc6 a6 4.c7+ axb5 5.cxd8=Q+ Rxd8 6.Nxd1 wins material.

134) 1.Nxf7 Kxf7 2.Nxc5 Bxc5 3.Bxc5 wins.

135) 1.Bb5! axb5 2.axb5 Q moves 3.Rxa8 winning the exchange.

136) 1.Nc7! Qxc7 2.Qxb5 wins the exchange.

137) 1.gxf5+ Bxf5 2.Rxf5! Rxf5 3.Rf1 Rf8 [what else?] **4.Rf3! Rf6 5.Kf2!** and White wins a piece by 6.Kg3 and 7.Kg4.

138) 1.Be7! Qxg4 2.Rxd8#.

139) 1.g4+! Kxg4 2.Be6.

140) 1.Qg1! [threat: 2.Rg8#] **1...Re8 2.Bh5! Rd8 3.Qh2** and now the Knight cannot be defended.

141) 1.Rd1! Qxc4 2.Rxd8+ K moves 3.bxc4 wins a Rook.

142) 1...Rxd5! 2.Rxd5 Qb7 3.Qg2 Qb1+! [But not 3...Nf4? because of 4.Rd8+] **4.Qg1 Qe4+ 5.Qg2 Qxg2+ 6. Kxg2 Nf4+** and Black wins a piece.

143) 1.c4! Ne7 [1...Nxc4 2.Rxd5] **2.c5** winning a piece.

144) 1.Bxe5 Qxe5 2.Qxe5 dxe5 3.Bxe6.

145) 1.Rxf4! exf4 2.Bh8!! and 3.Qg7# cannot be prevented.

146) 1.Qh4+! Kg8 2.Qg3+ Kh8 3.Bc3 wins the Queen.

147) 1.Qg8+!! Ke7 [after 1...Kxg8 2.Ng6!, mate by Rh8 is unstoppable] **2.Qxf7+ Kd8 3.Ng6 Qxb2 4.Rd1+ Bd7 5.Qxe8+!! Kxe8 6.Rh8#.**

148) 1...Qe7! and wins the Ne4 since 2.Ng3 allows 2...fxg3+.

149) 1.Nxd7 Rxd7 2.Bxd5! Rxd5 3.b6 wins a piece.

150) 1.Nd6! Re7 [1...Re6 2.Bb3] **2.Nhxf5 Bxf5 3.Nxf5 Re6 4.Bb3** winning material.

151) 1...Rxd2! 2.Qxd2 Nxe4 [Threatening 3...Ng3# and 3...Nxd2] **3.Qg2 Nf2#.**

152) 1.Re6!! [not 1.Rg6 because of 1...Rg8] **1...Qd8** [1...Qxe6 2.Qxf8#] **2.Rg6! Rg8 3.Rxf7 Rd1+ 4.Kh2 Qb8+ 5.g3 Rd2+ 6.Kh1.** Black's checks soon run out.

153) 1.Qb7! Rfc8 [on 1...Qd6 2.Nxe4 dxe4 3.Rxc6 wins] **2.Nxd5! Qd6 3.Rxc6!!** and now 3...Qxc6 loses to 4.Ne7+ and 5.Nxc6, while 3...Rxc6 loses to 4.Qxa8+ Nf8 5.Qxc6 Qxc6 6.Ne7+. Also if 4...Nb8, then 5.Ne7+ Qxe7 6.Qxb8+ Qf8 7.Qxa7 wins handily.

154) 1...Bg4 2.Qxg4 Nxf2+.

155) 1.Rxg7+!! Kxg7 [or 1...Qxg7 2.Rg1] **2.Rg1** winning.

156) 1...h4! 2.Nf1 [or 2.Nh1] **2...h3** and wins the Bishop.

157) 1...Nxc3! 2.bxc3 Rxc3+! 3.Qxc3 Rxb1#.

158) 1.Be4! Qxb7 2.Bxb7 wins material.

159) 1...Qxd7! 2.Nxd7 Bxc4.

160) 1.Qa8! retains the extra piece after 1...Qxc6 2.Qxb8+.

161) 1.Ne7+! Qxe7 2.Rxe7 and now 2...Rxh6 loses to 3.Re8#.

162) 1.Nc6 Qd7 2.Ne7+! Qxe7 3.Qxd5 wins the Exchange.

163) **1...Rg4!** [threatening simply 2...Bxf3+] **2.Bxg4 Qxf1#.**

164) **1.Nf7+!** **Rcxf7** [Rfxf7 amounts to the same thing] **2.exf7** and the Bg6 is lost since 3.Rxg6 cannot be stopped and 2...Bxf7 fails to 3.Qxg7#.

165) **1.Rxh6!** **gxh6 2.Rg1.**

166) **1.Bf4!** wins the pinned Nb8.

167) **1.Nd7!** **Nxd7 2.Qxe6+ Qxe6 3.Bxe6+ Rf7 4.Bxf7+** wins the exchange.

168) **1.Rg4!** wins the Queen as 1...Qxg4 allows 2.Qxf7+ and 3.Qxh7#.

169) **1.Bxd5!** **Bxd5** [not 1...cxd5 2.Rxa6] **2.Qxf6+** followed by 3.Qxe7.

170) **1...Rxa2!!** (a diversionary pin) **2.Qxa2 Qh5+ 3.Rh3 Qe5+ 4.Kh1 Qe1+ 5.Kh2 Qg1#.**

171) **1.Rc4! Ke7** [if 1...Kd7 then 2.Nc5+] **2.Rd4!** [to answer 2...Ke6 with 3.Nc5+ Ke6 4.Rxb4! Rxb4 5.Nd3+ and 6.Nxb4] **2...Kf8 3.g3!** [White creates a haven for his King so that Black cannot unpin with a timely Ra1+] **3...Kg7 4.Kg2 Kg6 5.Rc4! Kg7 6.Nd4 Kg6 7.Nc2** and the Bishop falls.

3. QUEEN SACRIFICE

Surely every chessplayer has dreamed of that classic moment in chess - the Queen sacrifice. Giving up the strongest piece on the board in a sweeping and often totally unexpected fashion is associated with some of the most impressive victories ever recorded. Usually the Queen sacrifice occurs as the crowning effort of a well conducted Kingside attack. There are also, however, examples of Queen sacrifices which allow a pawn to promote or which are a prelude to a win of enemy pieces in excess of the value of the Queen. In this last case it may be argued that it isn't really a sacrifice if more material is gained in return. Nonetheless, parting with the most powerful attacking piece in an unexpected manner is an esthetically pleasing conception.

172 /   1... ?

173 /   1... ?

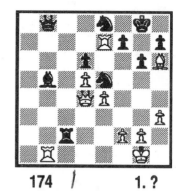

174 /   1. ?

175 \   1... ?

176 | 1... ?

177 √   1... ?

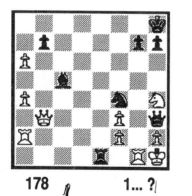

178   1... ?|

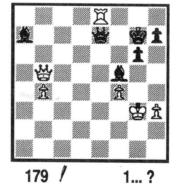

179 /   1... ?

180 | 1... ?

QUEEN SACRIFICE

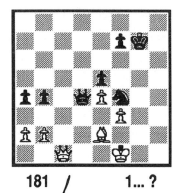

181 / 1... ?

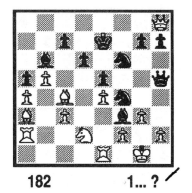

182 1... ? /

183 1... ? /

184 1... ? /

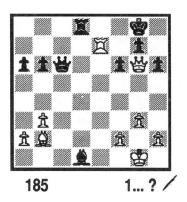

185 1... ? /

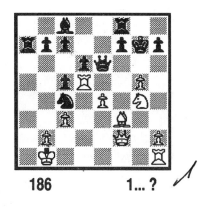

186 1... ? /

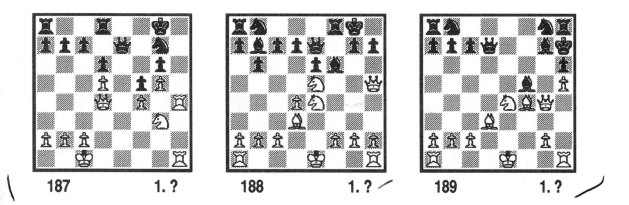

187 1. ?

188 1. ? /

189 1. ? /

QUEEN SACRIFICE

39

190 ✓   1. ?

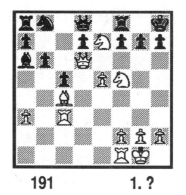

191   1. ?

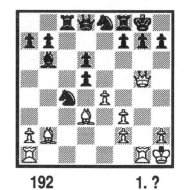

192   1. ?

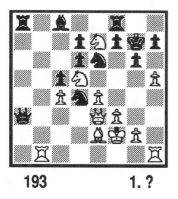

193   1. ?

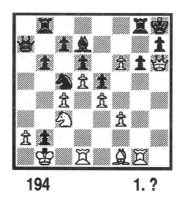

194   1. ?

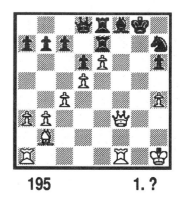

195   1. ?

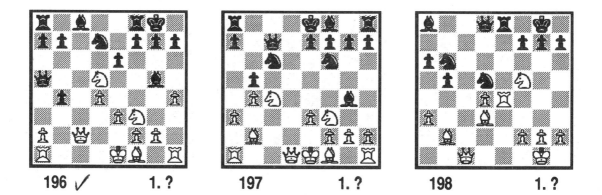

196 ✓   1. ?

197   1. ?

198   1. ?

QUEEN SACRIFICE

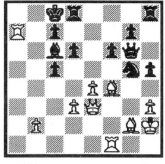

199   1. ?

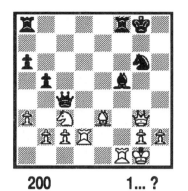

200   1... ?

201   1. ?

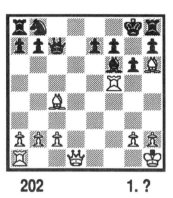

202   1. ?

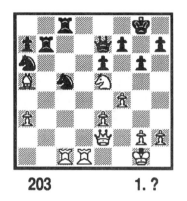

203   1. ?

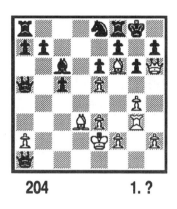

204   1. ?

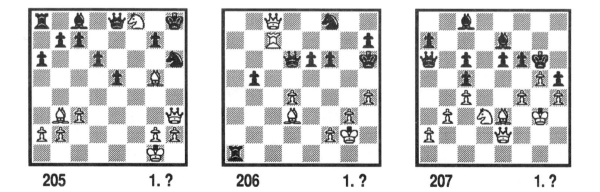

205   1. ?

206   1. ?

207   1. ?

QUEEN SACRIFICE

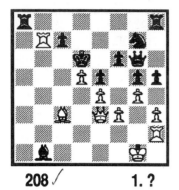

208 ✓   1. ?

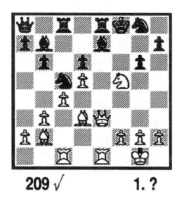

209 √   1. ?

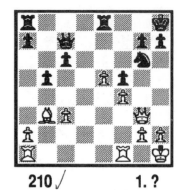

210 √   1. ?

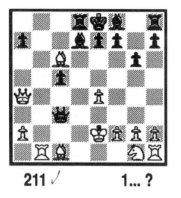

211 ✓   1... ?

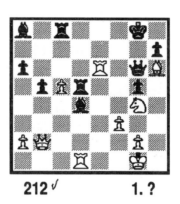

212 ✓   1. ?

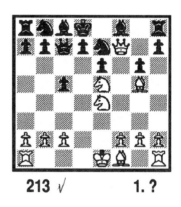

213 √   1. ?

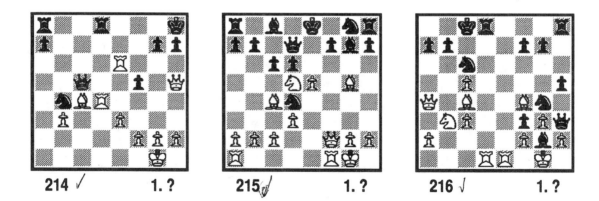

214 √   1. ?

215 √   1. ?

216 √   1. ?

QUEEN SACRIFICE

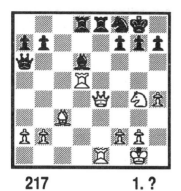

217   1. ?

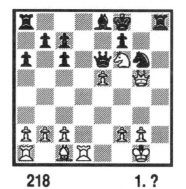

218   1. ?

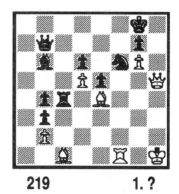

219   1. ?

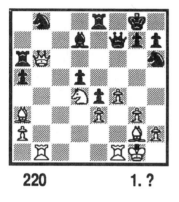

220   1. ?

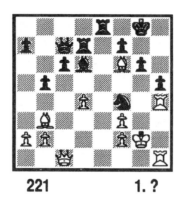

221   1. ?

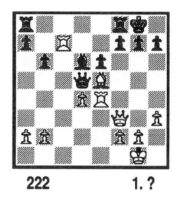

222   1. ?

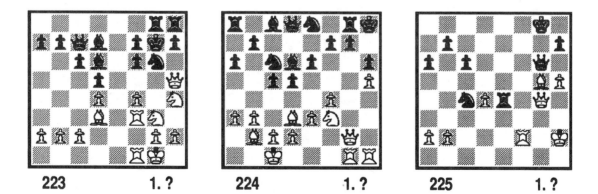

223   1. ?

224   1. ?

225   1. ?

QUEEN SACRIFICE

43

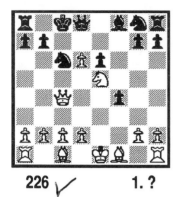

226 ✓   1. ?

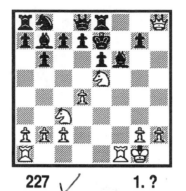

227 ✓   1. ?

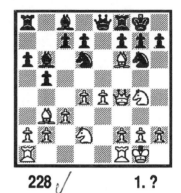

228 ✓   1. ?

229   1... ?

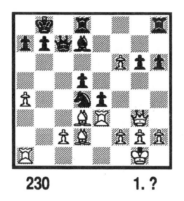

230   1. ?

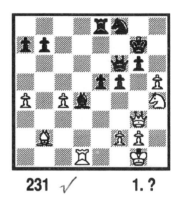

231 ✓   1. ?

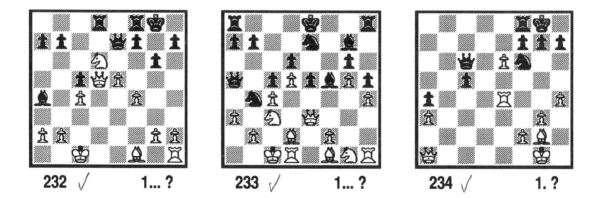

232 ✓   1... ?

233 ✓   1... ?

234 ✓   1. ?

QUEEN SACRIFICE

172) 1...Qg3+!! 2.Bxg3 hxg3+ 3.Kg4 Ne7 and wins. 4...Rg6+ is next.

173) 1...Qb5!! 2.Rd2 [2.Bxb5 Nb3#. If 2.Nxb5 then 2...Nb3# as the Bishop is now pinned!] **2...Nxc3!** [Now on 3.Bb5 Nb3#, and on 3.bxc3 comes 3...Qb1#, and finally, on 3.Qxc3 Nb3+].

174) 1.Rxb5! Qxb5 2.Qb6!! and wins.

175) 1...Qg3!! [The very famous sacrifice by the brilliant attacking master Frank Marshall] **2.Qxg3** [if 2.fxg3 then 2...Ne2+ 3.Kh1 Rxf1# or if 2.hxg3 then 2...Ne2#] **2...Ne2+ 3.Kh1 Nxg3+ 4.Kg1 Ne2+** and Black remains a piece ahead.

176) 1...Ng4! threatening 2...Qxh2#, and if 2.Qxh3 then 2...Nf2#.

177) 1...Rxd4!! 2.Nxd4 Qxe1+! 3.Qxe1 Bxd4+ 4.Kh1 [if 4.Kf1, then 4...Bc4+ 5.Be2 Nxh2#] **4...Nf2+ 5.Kg1 Nd3+** and after 6.Kf1 Nxe1 Black will be a piece up.

178) 1...Qf1! 2.Rxf1 Rxf1#.

179) 1...Qh4+!! 2.Kxh4 [on 2.Kf3 Qf2 is mate, or 2.Kg2 (or h2) and 2...Qf2+ 3.Kh1 Qg1#] **2...Bf2+ 3.Kg5 h6#.**

180) 1...Qh3!! forces mate since 2.gxh3 allows 2...Nxh3#.

181) 1...Qg1+! 2.Kxg1 Nxe2+ and wins.

182) 1...Qxh2+!! 2.Kxh2 Ng4+ 3.Kg1 Nh3+ 4.Kf1 Nh2#.

183) 1...Qxe6 2.Bxe6 Rxd1+ 3.Kf2 Ng4+ 4.Kf3 Nxh2+ 5.Kf2 Rf1#.

184) 1...Bxb3! 2.Bb2 [not 2.Nxb5 Nd4#] **2...Nb4+ 3.Kc1 Qxe5!** and now if 4.Rxe5 Nd3+ 5.Kb1 Nxf4 and if 4.Qxe5 Nd3+ 5.Kb1 Nxe5 and Black will remain a piece ahead.

185) 1...Qh1+!! 2.Kxh1 Bf3+ 3.Kg1 Rd1#.

186) 1...Qxd5! 2.exd5 Bf5+ 3.Qc2 [if 3.Kc1, then 3...Ra1#] **3...Ra1+! 4.Kxa1 Bxc2** and there is no defense to 5...Ra8#.

187) 1.Rh8+ Kf7 2.Qxg7+! Kxg7 3.R(h1)h7#.

188) 1.Qxh7+!! Kxh7 2.Nxf6+-+ Kh6 [2...Kh8 3.Ng6#] **3.Neg4+ Kg5 4.h4+ Kf4 5.g3+ Kf3 6.Be2+ Kg2 7.Rh2+ Kg1 8.Kd2#.**.

189) 1.Qg6+!! Bxg6 2.Ng5+! hxg5 3.hxg6#.

190) 1.Qxd7! Rxd7 2.Re8+ Kh7 3.Rcc8 and wins.

191) 1.Qg6!! fxg6 [if 1...hxg6 then 2.Rh3# or 1...Rg8 2.Qxh7+! Kxh7 3.Rh3#] **2.Nxg6+ hxg6 3.Rh3#.**

192) 1.Qxg7+! Nxg7 2.Rxg7+ Kh8 3.Rg8+-+! Kxg8 4.Rg1+ Qg5 5.Rxg5#.

193) 1.Qh6+!! Kxh6 [or 1...Kh8 2.Qxh7+! Kxh7 3.hxg6+ Kg7 4.Rh7#] **2.hxg6+ Kg5 3.Rh5+! Kxh5 4.f4+ Nxe2 5.Nf6+ Kh6 6.Rh1+ Kg7 7.Ne8+! Rxe8 8.Rxh7+ Kf6 9.Rxf7#.**

194) 1.Qxh7+! Kxh7 2.Rh1+ Bh3 3.Rxh3#.

195) 1.Qf7+! Rxf7 2.exf7#.

196) 1.Qxh7+! Kxh7 2.hxg5+ Kg6 [2...Kg8 3.Ne7#] **3.Ne7#.**

197) **1.Nce5! Nxe5 2.Nxe5! Bxd1 3.Bxb5+ Nd7** [on 3...Kd8 White wins with 4.Rxd1+ Kc8 5.Ba6+ Kb8 6.Nc6+! Qxc6 7.Be5+ Qd6 8.Rc1! and mate follows] **4.Bxd7+ Qxd7** [or 4...Kd8 5.Rxd1 winning easily] **5.Nxd7** winning a pawn.

198) **1.Qg5! g6** [1...Qxg5 2.Rxe8#] **2.Qh6! gxf5 3.Rg4+! fxg4 4.Bxh7+ Kh8 5.Bg6+ Kg8 6.Qh7+ Kf8 7.Qxf7#.**

199) **1.Qxc5! dxc5 2.Rxc7+ Kb8 3.Rxg7+ Kc8 4.Rxg6** and White wins several pawns.

200) **1...Qxf1+! 2.Kxf1 Bd3+-+ 3.Ke1 Rf1#.**

201) **1.Qxf3! Qxf3 2.Nd7+ Ka8 3.Nc6+ Na6 4.Nb6#.**

202) **1.Qd5! e6 2.Qxe6! fxe6! 3.Bxe6+ Qf7 4.Rxf6! Qxe6 5.Rf8#.**

203) **1.Qxa6! Nxa6 2.Rxc8+ Kg7 3.Ng4** [threatening 4.Bc3+] **3...Qxa3 4.Bc3+ f6 5.Bxf6+ Kf7 6.Rh8 Qb4 7.Rxh7+ Kg8 8.Rd8+ Kxh7 9.Rh8#.**

204) **1.Qxh7+! Kxh7 2.Rh3+ Kg8 3.Rh8#.**

205) **1.Qxh6+! gxh6 2.Bf6#.**

206) **1.Qxf8+ Qxf8 2.Rxh7#.**

207) **1.f5+! exf5** [1...Kxf5 2.Qf3+ wins after 2...Kg6 3.Qxh5+! Kg7 4.g6 - this is similar to the main line] **2.Qxh5+! Kg7** [2...Kxh5 3.Nf4#] **3.g6 Kg8 4.Qh7+ Kf8 5.Qf7#.**

208) **1.Qb6+! Ke7** [on 1...cxb6 2.Bb4#] **2.d6+ Kf8 3.dxc7** and Black's position is hopeless.

209) **1.Bg7+! Kf7 2.Qe6+! Nxe6 3.dxe6#.**

210) **1.Qxg6!! hxg6 2.Rf3 and 3.Rh3** will be mate.

211) **1...Qd3+!! 2.Kxd3** [2.Ke1 Qxb1] **2...Bxc6+** followed by 3...Bxa4.

212) **1.Qxd4! Rxd4** [not 1...Qxe6 2.Qg7#] **2.Rxg6+ hxg6 3.Rxd4** and White is material ahead.

213) **1.Qe8+! Kxe8 2.Nf6+ Kd8 3.Nf7#.**

214) **1.Qxh7+! Kxh7 2.Rh4+ Kg8 3.Re8#.**

215) **1.Nc7+! Qxc7** [or 1...Kf8 2.e6 Qxc7 3.e7+ Nxe7 4.Qxf7#] **2.Bxf7+ Kd7 3.Qf5+! Nxf5 4.e6#.**

216) **1.Qxc6+! bxc6 2.Ba6#.**

217) **1.Rg5! Rxe4** [if 1...Ng6, then 2.Qxe8+ Rxe8 3.Rxe8+ Bf8 4.h5! and if 4...Nh8 then 5.Rxg7#. If 1...g6, then 2.Nh6#] **2.Nh6+ Kh8 3.Bxg7#.**

218) **1.Qh6+! Ke7** [on 1...Rxh6 2.Bxh6+ Ke7 3.Ng8#] **2.Ng8+! Rxg8 3.Bg5+ f6 4.exf6+ Kf7 5.Qh7+ Kf8 6.Bh6+ Rg7 7.Qxg7#.**

219) **1.Qh7+! Kf8** [after 1...Nxh7 2.gxh7+ Kh8 3.Rf8 is mate] **2.Qh8+ Ke7 3.Qxg7+ Kd8 4.Qxb7** wins material.

220) **1.Qxb8! Rxb8 2.Rxb8+ Be8 3.Bh3!** [3.Rc1? Ng4 with the idea of 4...Nf6] **3...Kh8** [3...g6 is follow by 4.Rc1 and 5.Rc8] **4.Rc1 Ng8 5.Rcc8 Nf6 6.Bf1** wins.

221) **1.Qxf4! Bxf4 2.Rxh5 gxh5 3.Rxh5** and mate by Rh8.

222) **1.Rd7! Rad8 2.Rxd6! Rxd6 3.Qf6!** and now after 3...gxf6 4.Rg4+ Kh8 5.Bxf6#.

48

223) 1.Qh6+! Kxh6 2.Nhf5+ Bxf5 3.Nxf5+ Kh5 4.g4+ Kxg4 5.Rg3+ Kh5 6.Be2#.

224) 1.Bh7!! Kxh7 2.Qg6+! fxg6 [2...Kh8 3.Qxh6#] **3.hxg6+ Kh8 4.Rxh6#.**

225) 1.Bh6! and now if either 1...Qxg4 or 1...Rxg4, then 2.Rf8 is checkmate.

226) 1.Qxc6+! bxc6 [1...Kb8 2.Nd7+ forces Black to give up the Queen] **2.Ba6+ Kb8 3.Nxc6#.**

227) 1. Qxg7+! Bxg7 2.Rf7+ Kd6 3.Nb5+ Kd5 4.c4+ Ke4 5.Re1#.

228) 1.Qh6! gxh6 [1...gxf6 2.Nxf6+ Kh8 3.Qxh7#] **2.Nxh6#.**

229) 1...Nd3! 2.Qf5 Ne1!! [with the idea of Nf3#!] **3.Kf1 Nc2+!** [on 3...gxf5 4.Bxe1] **4.Bc1** [on 4.Ke2 Nd4+ winning] **4...Rxc1+ 5.Ke2 Nd4+ 6.Kd2 Nb3+** and Black wins.

230) 1.Re4! Qxg3 [if 1...dxe4 2.Bf4 winning] **2.Rxd4! Qg4 3.Rxg4 Bxg4 4.Bxg6 Rhg8 5.Bh7 Rh8 6.Bd3 Rde8 7.f7 Re7 8.f8=Q+ Rxf8 9.Bb4** winning.

231) 1.Rxd4 f4 [on 1...exd4 2.Bxd4! Qxd4 3.Nxf5+ and wins] **2.Rxf4!** winning.

232) 1...Rxd6! 2.Qxd6 [2.exd6 is met with 2...Qe1+] **2...Rd8!!**

233) 1...Qa4!! 2.Bd3 [2.Nxa4 Na2#] **2...Bxd3** and wins.

234) 1.Qxf6! gxf6 [1...Qxe4 2.Qxf7+!] **2.Rg4+** winning a piece.

4. OVERLOADING

Overloading involves the exploitation of an enemy unit which must protect at least two other important pieces (or squares). The object of the attacker is to force the overloaded defending piece to relinquish its necessary defensive functions. Typically this is accomplished by attacking one of the defensive piece's "dependents" and thereby making the defender give up the protection of its other obligation (s). Often the defending piece is forced to leave its home square in order to protect one of its pieces or squares which in turn gives up its protection of another piece or square.

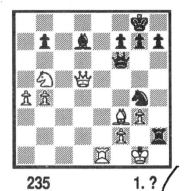

235   1. ?

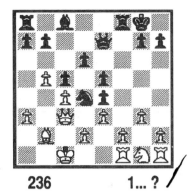

236   1... ?

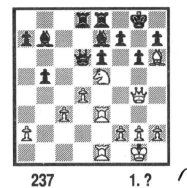

237   1. ?

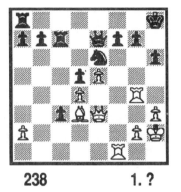

238   1. ?

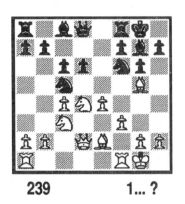

239   1... ?

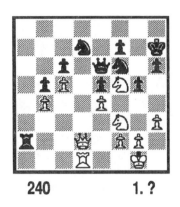

240   1. ?

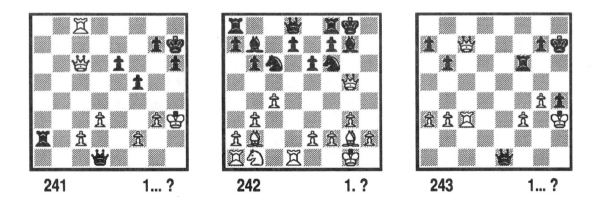

241   1... ?   242   1. ?   243   1... ?

OVERLOADING

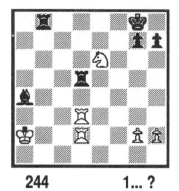

244   1... ?

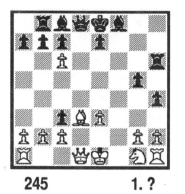

245   1. ?

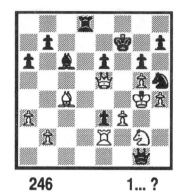

246   1... ?

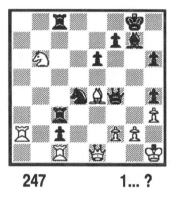

247   1... ?

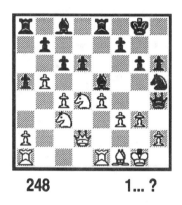

248   1... ?

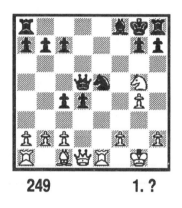

249   1. ?

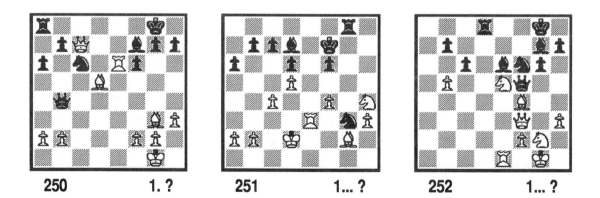

250   1. ?   251   1... ?   252   1... ?

OVERLOADING

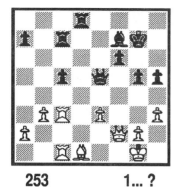

253   1... ?

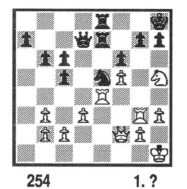

254   1. ?

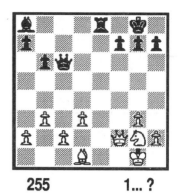

255   1... ?

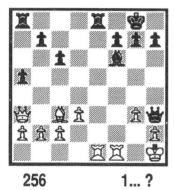

256   1... ?

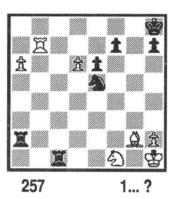

257   1... ?

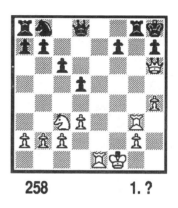

258   1. ?

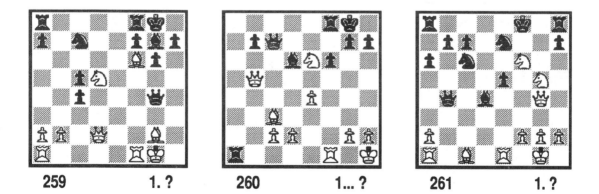

259   1. ?

260   1... ?

261   1. ?

OVERLOADING

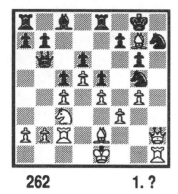

262   1. ?

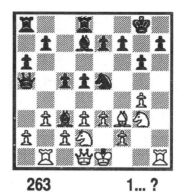

263   1... ?

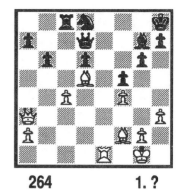

264   1. ?

265 ✓   1. ?

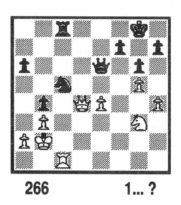

266   1... ?

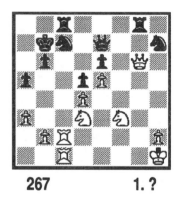

267   1. ?

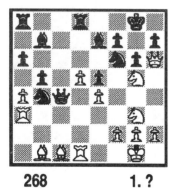

268   1. ?

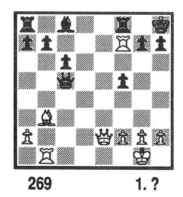

269   1. ?

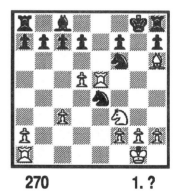

270   1. ?

OVERLOADING

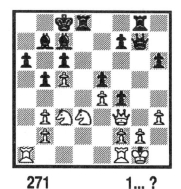

271   1... ?

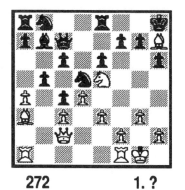

272   1. ?

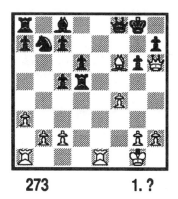

273   1. ?

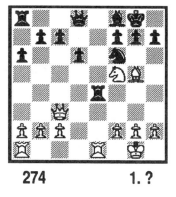

274   1. ?

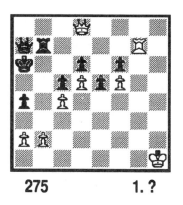

275   1. ?

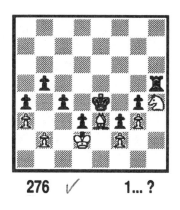

276 ✓   1... ?

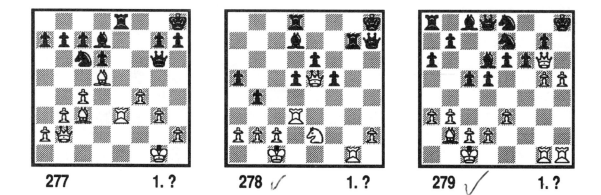

277   1. ?

278 ✓   1. ?

279 ✓   1. ?

OVERLOADING

280   1... ?

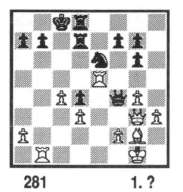

281   1. ?

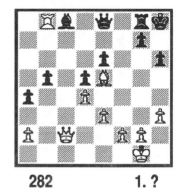

282   1. ?

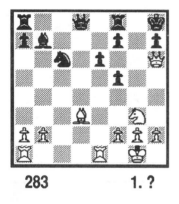

283   1. ?

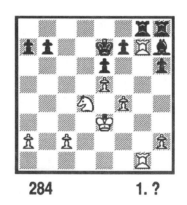

284   1. ?

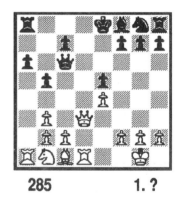

285   1. ?

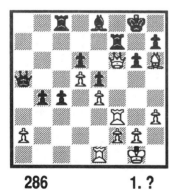

286   1. ?

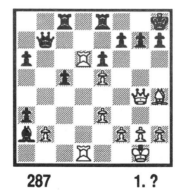

287   1. ?

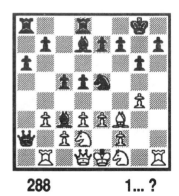

288   1... ?

OVERLOADING

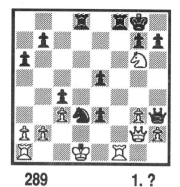

289   1. ?

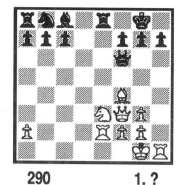

290   1. ?

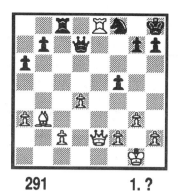

291   1. ?

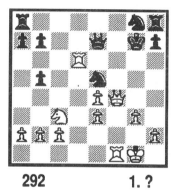

292   1. ?

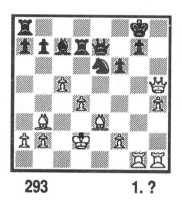

293   1. ?

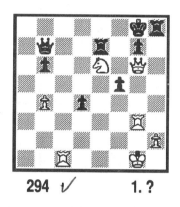

294 ✓   1. ?

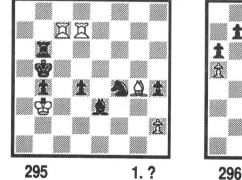

295   1. ?

296   1. ?

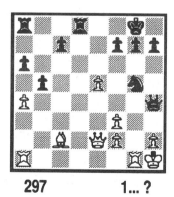

297   1... ?

OVERLOADING

57

235) 1.Qc5!! [Black had the ugly threat of Rh1+!! which is now impossible because of Bxh1 and there is no mate on f2. Besides this defensive function, 1.Qc5!! overloads the Bishop on d7 by threatening 2.Qc8+! Bxc8 3.Re8#. Black must defend against the mate and in so doing, loses a Rook] **1...h5 2.Bxg4 hxg4 3.Kxh2 Qh6+ 4.Kg1 Bc6 5.f3 Bxf3 6.Re8+ Kh7 7.Qc2+!** and Black resigns, as a trade of Queens will be forced by 8.Qh2.

236) 1...Bh3! 2.Re1 [on 2.Nxh3 comes 2...Ne2+] **1...Bg2** winning material.

237) 1.Nxg6! hxg6 2.Rxe6 Qd7 [if 2...fxe6 3.Qxg6+ winning] **3.Rxg6+ Kh7 4.Ree6 Bf6** [4...fxe6 5.Rg7+ Kh8 6.Qg6 and wins] **5.Rgxf6 Rg8 6.Bg5 Rg7 7.Rh6+ Kg8 8.Qh5** and White wins.

238) 1.Rf6! Ng5 [1...Nf8 2.Qxh6+] **2.Rxg5 hxg5 3.Qxg5 Kg8** [3...gxf6 4.Qh6+ winning] **4.Qh4! Qa3 5.Rf3 g6 6.Bxg6 c2 7.Bxc2 Qxf3 8.Qh7!+ Kf8 9.gxf3.**

239) 1...Nfxe4! 2.Nxe4 Nxe4 3.fxe4 Bxd4+ 4.Qxd4 [4.Kh1 Qb6!]**4...Qxg5 5.Qxd6 Qe3+ 6.Rf2 Be6! 7.Qf4 Qxf4 8.Rxf4 Rad8 9.Bf1 Rd4!**

240) 1.Nxg5+ hxg5 2.Qxg5 Ne8 3.Rd6!! and wins.

241) 1...Rxc2!! and White will lose material or be mated on h1.

242) 1.Rxd7! and if 1...Qxd7 2.Bxf6 winning. Obviously 1...Nxd7 is met with 2.Qxg7#.

243) 1...Rf7! winning, as 2.Qxf7 is met with 2...Qg3#. Other White Queen moves leave the Rc3 open to capture.

244) 1...Ra5! 2.Ra3 Bb3+ 3.Kb2 Bxe6+.

245) 1.Qh5+! Rxh5 2.Bg6#.

246) 1...Rd4+! 2.Qxd4 Qh2 and **3...Qg3** mates.

247) 1...Ne2! 2.Rcxc2 [or 2.Nxc8 Rxh3+! and mates as in the main line. Also 2.Qxe2? hangs the Rc1] **2...Rxh3+! 3.gxh3 Qxe4+ 4.f3 Qxf3+ 5.Kh2 Be5#.**

248) 1...Nxg3! 2.hxg3 Qxg3+ 3.Bg2 Bh3! [threatening 4...Bxd4+ since 5.Qxd4 allows mate at g2] **4.Re2 Qh2+ 5.Kf1 Qh1+ 6.Kf2 Qxg2+ and wins.**

249) 1.Rxe5! Qxe5 2.Qf3 Qf6 3.Qd5+ and mate next.

250) 1.Re8+! Rxe8 [1...Qf8 2.Qxf7+] **2.Qxf7+ Kh8 3.Qxe8+ Qf8 4.Qxf8#.**

251) 1...Nf5! 2.Nxf5 Rxg2+ and **3...Bxf5.**

252) 1...Bd5! 2.Qd3 [2.Qe3 Bxg2 3.Kxg2 Nd5 forks the Queen and Bf4, or 2.Qg3 Bxg2 3.Kxg2 Nh5 in the same manner, or finally if 2.Ne3, then 2...Qxe5! wins a piece] **2...Qxd3 3.Nxd3 Bxg2 4.Kxg2 Rxd3.**

253) 1...Rxd1+ 2.Rxd1 Qxc3.

254) 1.Rxg7!! Rxg7 2.Nxf6 Qe7 3.Nxe8 Qxe8 4.Qf4! Re7 5.f6! Ng6 [5...Re6 6.Rxe5! Rxe5 7.f7! threatening 8.Qf6#] **6.Rxe7 Nxe7 7.f7! Qf8 8.Qf6+ Qg7 9.f8=Q+ wins.**

255) 1...Re1+!! and if 2.Qxe1 Qxg2#, while 2.Nxe1 fails to 2...Qh1#.

256) 1...Re2! threatens mate at h2, but 2.Rxe2 allows 2...Qxf1#.

257) 1...Nf3! threatening 2...Rxf1+! 3.Bxf1 Rxh2#, and the defense 2.Bxf3 allows 2...Rxf1#.

258) 1.Re8! Qxe8 [1...Rxe8 2.Qg7#] **2.Qf6+ Rg7 3.Qxg7#.**

259) 1.Qh6! Bxh6 2.Ne7#.

260) 1...Qd7!! 2.Qc4 [2.Qxd7 Rxf1#] **2...Rxf1+ 3.Qxf1 Qxe6.**

261) 1.Ba3 Qxa3 2.Qe6! Nd8 3.Qf7+!! Nxf7 4.Ne6#!

262) 1.Bf6! [threatening 2.Qh6 Nxf6 3.Qh8#] **1...Nxf6 2.Qh8#.**

263) 1...Nxf3+ 2.Qxf3 Bxd2+.

264) 1.Qxa7! Qxa7 [1...Rc7 2.Qxc7 Qxc7 3.Re8+ as in our main line] **2.Re8+ Bf8 3.Bd4+ Qg7 4.Rxf8#.**

265) 1.Qxd7! winning, since 1...Rxd7 allows 2.Rxe8# and 1...Qxd7 loses to 2.Rdxd7 retaining the extra piece.

266) 1...Qe5! 2.Rc4 [on 2.Qxe5 Nd3+ and 3...Rxc1#] **2...Nd3+ 3.Kb1** [3.Kc2 Qxd4] **3...Qxd4 4.Rxd4 Rc1#.**

267) 1.Rxc7+ wins since 1...Qxc7 loses to 2.Rxc7+ Kxc7 3.Qxh7+ and 1...Rxc7 allows 2.Rxc7+ and 3.Qxg8.

268) 1.Nh5! gxh5 [on 1...Nxh5 2.Qxh7+ and 3.Qxf7#] **2.Rg3 Bf8** [or 2...h4 3.Ne6+ hxg3 4.Qg7#] **3.Nxh7+ Ng4 4.Nf6#.**

269) 1.Qe5! threatening both the Queen and mate on g7, and 1...Qxe5 loses to 2.Rxf8#.

270) 1.Nd2! d6 [1...Nxd2 2.Rg5#] **2.Nxe4! dxe5** [2...Nxe4 3.Re8#] **3.Nxf6#.**

271) 1...Rxd3! 2.Qxd3 Qxg2#.

272) 1.Bd6! wins since 1...Qxd6 loses to 2.Nxf7#.

273) 1.Re8! Qxe8 2.Qg7#.

274) 1.Nh6+! gxh6 [1...Kh8 2.Nxf7+] **2.Bxf6** and 3.Qg3+ wins.

275) 1.Qe8! Ka5 [1...Rxg7 2.Qb5#] **2.Qc6! Rxg7 3.Qb5#.**

276) 1...b4! 2.axb4 Rxh4 3.gxh4 g3! 4.fxg3 c3+! 5.bxc3 a3 and now after 6.Kc1, simply 6...Kxe3 wins easily.

277) 1.f5! Qg5 [1...Qxf5 2.Bg7# or 1...Bxf5 2.Bxg7+ Qxg7 3.Rxe8#] **2.Bxg7+! Qxg7 3.f6 Qg6 4.f7+ Ne5 5.Rxe5! dxe5 6.Qxe5+! Qg7** [6...Rxe5 7.f8=Q+] **7.Qxe8+ Bxe8 8.fxe8=Q+ Qg8 9.Qxg8#.**

278) 1.Rh3! Qxh3 2.Qxg7#.

279) 1.gxf6! Nxg6 2.hxg6+ Kg8 3.Rh8+! Kxh8 4.f7! Be7 5.Rh1+ Bh4 6.f8=Q#.

280) 1...Rg6+ 2.Kh2 Qd2+! 3.Bxd2 Rf2+ 4.Qg2 R[either] xg2#.

281) 1.Rc5+! Kb8 [1...Rc7 2.Rxc7+ Kxc7 3.Rxb7+ wins, or 1...Nc7 2.Qxf4] **2.Bxb7! Rxb7** [2...Qxg3+ is answered by 3.Bg2+!] **3.Rxb7+ Kxb7 4.Qg2+ Kb8 5.Rb5+ Kc7 6.Qb7+ Kd6 7.Rd5#.**

282) 1.Rxc8! Qxc8 2.Qg6 and there is no defense to 3.Qxh6#.

283) 1.Bxf5 exf5 2.Nxf5 Rg8 3.Re8! Qxe8 [3...Rxe8 4.Qg7#] **4.Qf6+ mates.**

284) **1. Rxh7!** wins a piece, since 1...Rxg1 allows 2.Rxh8 and 1...Rxh7 loses to 2.Rxg8.

285) **1.Rxa6!** wins, as 1...Rxa6 allows 2.Qd8# and 1...Qxa6 allows 2.Qd7#.

286) **1.Qe7! Qc7** [1...Rxe7 2.Rf8# or 1...Rxf3 2.Qg7#] **2.Qf8+! Rxf8 3.Rxf8#.**

287) **1.Bf6! gxf6** [1...Rg8 2.Qxg7+! Rxg7 3.Rd8+ Rxd8 4.Rxd8#] **2.exf6 Rg8 3.Rd8! Rcxd8 4.Rxd8** and 5.Qg7# cannot be prevented.

288) **1...Nxf3+ 2.Qxf3 Qxb1+.**

289) **1.Qd5+! Rxd5 2.Rxf8#.**

290) **1.Nd5 Qd8 2.Bxc7 Qd7 3.Qg4! Re6 4.Rxe6 Qxe6** [4...fxe6 5.Nf6+] **5.Nf6+ Kf8** [5...Qxf6 6.Qxc8 mates] **6.Bd6+! Qxd6 7.Qxc8+ Ke7 8.Ng8#.**

291) **1.Qc4!** [threatening 2.Qg8#] **1...Rxc4 2.Rxf8#.**

292) **1.Rd7! Qxd7** [1...Nxd7 2.Qg4+ Kh6 3.Rf5 Nf6 4.Qg5#] **2.Qxe5+ Kg6 3.Rf5 h6 4.Qxh8** and wins.

293) **1.Rxg7+ Qxg7** [1...Kxg7 2.Bxe6 Qxe6 3.Rg1+ mates] **2.Bxe6+ Rf7 3.Rg1! Qxg1 4.Qxf7+ Kh8 5.Qh5+ Kg7 6.Qh6#.**

294) **1.Rc8+! Qxc8 2.Qxg7+! Rxg7 3.Rxg7#.**

295) **1.Rd5+! Nxd5** [1...Ka6 2.Bc8+] **2.Be2+ Ka5 3.Ra7+ Ra6 4.Rxa6#.**

296) **1.Re5 Qd7 2.Rxe8+ Qxe8 3.d7! Qxd7 4.Qb8+ Kh7 5.Qh8+! Nxh8 6.Rg7#.**

297) **1...Rd2! 2.Qxd2 Nxf3** threatens both the Queen and mate.

5. KNIGHT FORK

The late Dr. Robert R. McCready, a strong expert and beloved chessplayer in Dallas for many years used to jokingly say, "Were it not for those darned Knights, I would have been a Grandmaster." Indeed, of all the chess pieces the Knight is the most fascinating and mysterious. Its singular ability to hop over all obstacles, both friend and foe, set it apart. Potentially the Knight can attack up to seven pieces at once. In reality it is rare to encounter a Knight fork against more than two enemy units. The Knight fork is quite often prepared by a preliminary sacrifice or diversionary move. In any event, the Knight is very often the source of intriguing tactical play as it leaps unexpectedly into the thick of things.

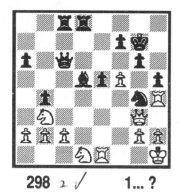 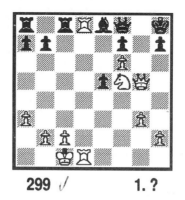 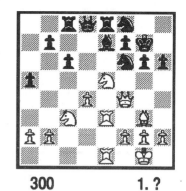

298 2 ✓   1... ?   299 ✓   1. ?   300   1. ?

 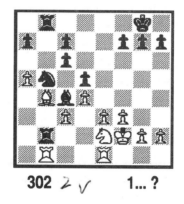 

301 1 ✓   1. ?   302 2 ✓   1... ?   303 1 ✓   1... ?

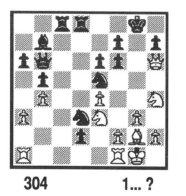 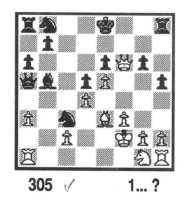 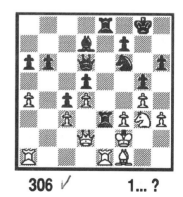

304   1... ?   305 ✓   1... ?   306 ✓   1... ?

KNIGHT FORK

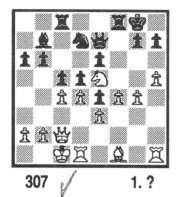 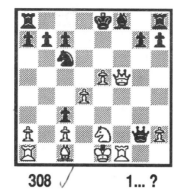 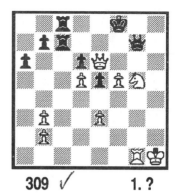

307 ✓   1. ?   308 ✓   1... ?   309 ✓   1. ?

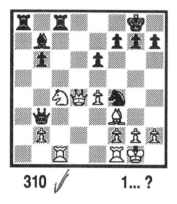 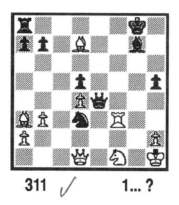 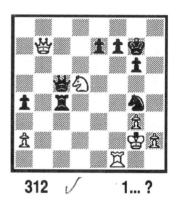

310 ✓   1... ?   311 ✓   1... ?   312 ✓   1... ?

 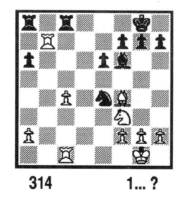 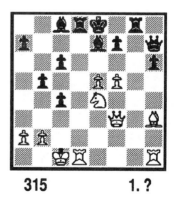

313   1... ?   314   1... ?   315   1. ?

KNIGHT FORK

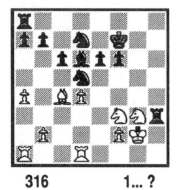

316 1... ?

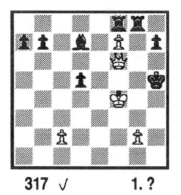

317 √ 1. ?

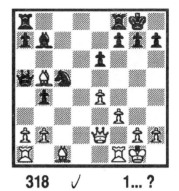

318 √ 1... ?

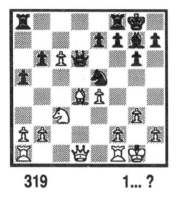

319 1... ?

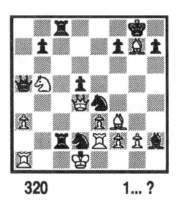

320 1... ?

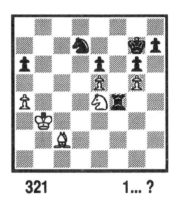

321 1... ?

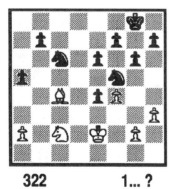

322 1... ?

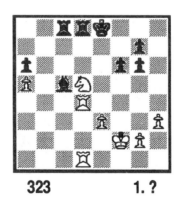

323 1. ?

324 1... ?

KNIGHT FORK

325   1... ?

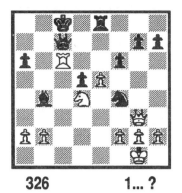

326   1... ?

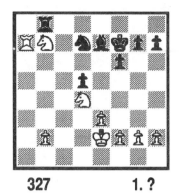

327   1. ?

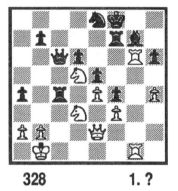

328   1. ?

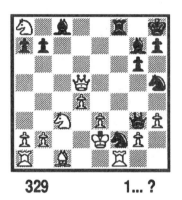

329   1... ?

330   1... ?

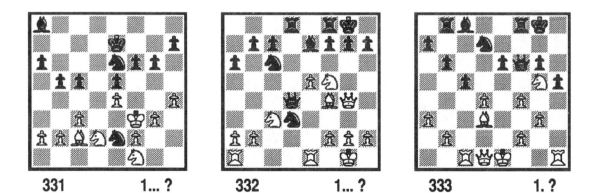

331   1... ?

332   1... ?

333   1. ?

KNIGHT FORK

334   1.... ?

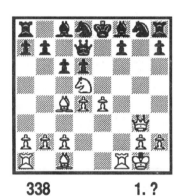

335   1. ?

336   1... ?

337   1. ?

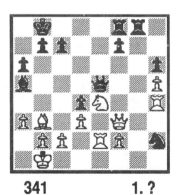

338   1. ?

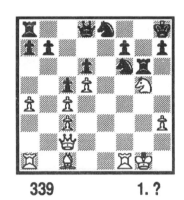

339   1. ?

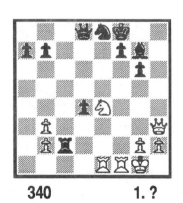

340   1. ?

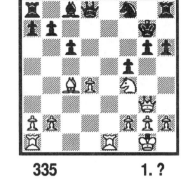

341   1. ?

342   1... ?

KNIGHT FORK

343 ✓   1. ?

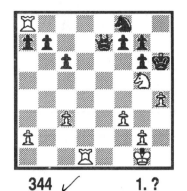

344 ✓   1. ?

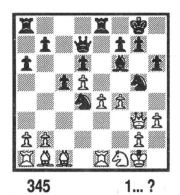

345   1... ?

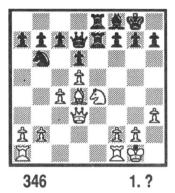

346   1. ?

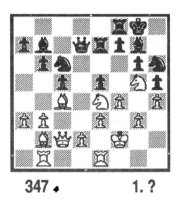

347   1. ?

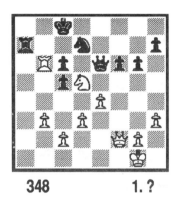

348   1. ?

349   1. ?

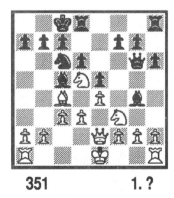

350   1. ?

351   1. ?

KNIGHT FORK

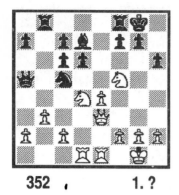

352 .   1. ?

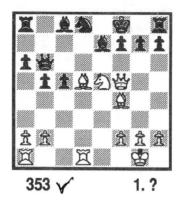

353 ✓   1. ?

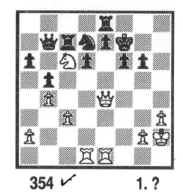

354 ✓   1. ?

355 ✓   1... ?

356 ✓   1. ?

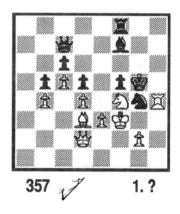

357 ✓   1. ?

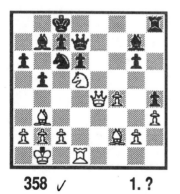

358 ✓   1. ?

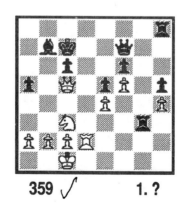

359 ✓   1. ?

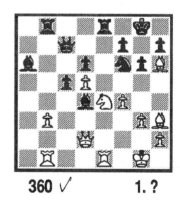

360 ✓   1. ?

KNIGHT FORK

70

361 ✓   1... ?

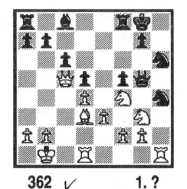

362 ✓   1. ?

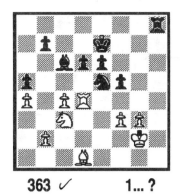

363 ✓   1... ?

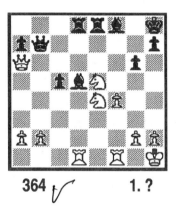

364 ✓   1. ?

365 ✓   1... ?

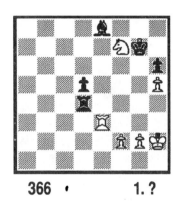

366 •   1. ?

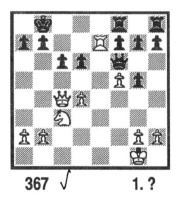

367 ✓   1. ?

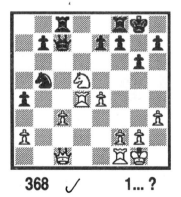

368 ✓   1... ?

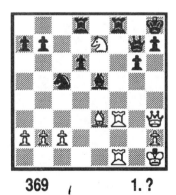

369 ,   1. ?

KNIGHT FORK

370 ✓   1. ?

371 ✓   1. ?

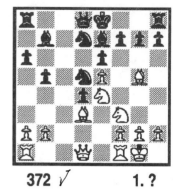

372 √   1. ?

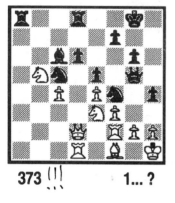

373 (!!)   1... ?

374 ✓   1. ?

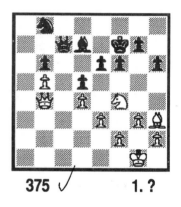

375 √   1. ?

376 ✓   1. ?

KNIGHT FORK

72

298) 1...Bxg2+! 2.Qxg2 Rxd1 3.Rxd1 [if 3.Qxc6 Rxe1+ and wins] **3...Nf2+ 4.Kg1 Qxg2+ 5.Kxg2 Nxd1** and Black wins.

299) 1.Qg7+! Qxg7 2.fxg7+ Kg8 3.Ne7+ wins.

300) 1.Qxh6+! Kxh6 [1...Kg8 2.Bh4 N(8)h7 3.Nxg6 winning] **2.Nxf7+ Kg7 3.Nxd8** and wins material.

301) 1.Nf6+ Kf7 2.Qxg7+! Kxg7 3.Ne8+! and wins.

302) 1...Rxb1 2.Rxb1 Bxe2 3.Kxe2 Nxc3+ wins the Rb1 after 4.Bxc3 Rxb1.

303) 1...Rxh2+ 2.Kxh2 Nxf3+ 3.K anywhere Nxd2 with two extra pawns.

304) 1...Nxf2! 2.Rxf2 [2.Kxf2 Ng4+ wins White's Queen or 2.Bf3, Nfg4 3.Bxg4 Nxg4 wins easily] **2...Rc1+ 3.Bf1 Rxa1 4.Nhf5 exf5 5.Nxf5 Qxf2+! 6.Kxf2 Ng4+ and 7...Nxh6 wins.**

305) 1...Ne4+! 2.fxe4 Rf8 wins the Queen.

306) 1...Qxg3+ 2.Kxg3 Ne4+ 3.K anywhere Nxd2.

307) 1.Ng6! hxg6 2.hxg6 Rf6 [on 2...Nf6 3.Qh2 forces mate at h8] **3.Rh8+! Kxh8 4.Qh2+ Kg8 5.Qh7+ Kf8 6.Qh8#.**

308) 1...Qxe2+! 2.Kxe2 Nxd4+ and **3...Nxf5.**

309) 1.Qxc8+ Rxc8 2.Ne6+.

310) 1...Qxf3! 2.gxf3 Ne2+ 3. K moves Nxd4.

311) 1...Nf2+ wins the Queen.

312) 1...Qxd5+! 2.Qxd5 Ne3+ 3. K moves Nxd5 wins a piece.

313) 1...d4! now if the Nc3 moves, then 2...Nb3+ wins the White Queen since the c-pawn is pinned.

314) 1...Nc5 2.Rbb1 Nd3 and 3...Nxf4.

315) 1.Nf6+ Bxf6 2.exf6 and now if 2...Bd7 then 3.Qe3+ wins, since 3...Be6 is forced [3...Kf8 4.Qe7#].

316) 1...Rxg3+ 2.fxg3 Ne3+ and after 3...Nxc4 Black has two pieces plus a pawn for a Rook and every chance of winning.

317) 1.fxg8=N! Rxf6+ 2.Nxf6+ K moves 3.Nxd7.

318) 1...Nb3! 2.axb3 [if 2.Rb1 then 2...Nd4 forks Qe2 and Bb5] **2...Qxa1** winning the exchange.

319) 1...Qxd4 2.Qxd4 Nf3+ 3.K moves Nxd4.

320) 1...Rc1+! 2.Rxc1 Rxc1+ 3.Kxc1 Nb3+ 4.K moves Nxd4.

321) 1...Rxe4 2.Bxe4 Nc5+ and 3...Nxe4.

322) 1...b5 2.Bxb5 [if 2.Bb3, then 2... a4 traps the Bishop] **2...N(either) d4+ 3.Nxd4 Nxd4+** and 4...Nxb5.

74

323) 1.Nc7+ Ke7 2.Rxd8 Rxd8 3.Rxd8 Kxd8 4.Ne6+ and 5.Nxc5.

324) 1...d2+ 2.Kxd2 Nxe4+ 3.K moves Nxd6.

325) 1...Rd2 2.Qc1 [2.Qxd2 Nf3+] **2...Nf3+ 3.Kf1** [3.Kh1 Rxh2#] **3...Qb5+ 4.Qc4 Qxc4#.**

326) 1...Qxc6 2.Nxc6 Ne2+.

327) 1.Nd6+! Bxd6 2.Rxd7+ Be7 3.Rxe7+ Kxe7 4.Nc6+ and 5.Nxb8.

328) 1.Nxe5 Bxe5 [or 1...dxe5 2.Rxc6] **2.Rg8#.**

329) 1...Nf4+! 2.exf4 Re8+ 3.Ne4 [3.Kd2 Qd3#] **3...Rxe4+ 4.Qxe4** [4.Kd2 Qd3#] **4...Nxe4** wins.

330) 1...Nh3+ 2.Kg2 [hoping for 2...Rxf3 3.Kxh3] **2...Ng5** wins a piece.

331) 1...N(e2)d4+ 2.cxd4 Nxd4+ 3.K moves Nxc2.

332) 1...Qxf2+ 2.Kh1 Qxe1+! 3.Rxe1 Nf2+ 4.Kg1 Nxg4 wins.

333) **1.Nh7! Qg7** [1...Kxh7 2.Qxh5+ Kg8 (or g7) 3.Qh7#) **2.Nxf8** wins the exchange.

334) 1...Bh3! 2.Kh1 [2.gxh3 Nf3+ or 2.f4 Qg6! threatening 3...Qxg2# as well as 3...Nf3+ and 4...Nxd4] **2...Bxg2+! 3.Kxg2 Qf3+ 4.Kg1 Qg4+ 5.Kh1 Nf3 6.Qd1 Qh3** and mate or loss of the Queen is forced.

335) 1.Re8!! Qg5 [1...Qxe8 2.Nh5+ Kh7 3.Nf6+ and 4.Nxe8+] **2.Qe3 h5 3.Qe5+** winning, as 3...Qf6 loses to 4.Re7+ and 3...Kh6 drops the Rh8.

336) 1...Rxc1 2.h3 [2.Qxc1 Qxg2# or 2.Rxc1 Nf3+] **2...Nf3+ 3.Kf2 Rxf1+** and 4...Nxd2.

337) 1. Qf8+! Rxf8 2.Rxf8+ Kxf8 3.Nxd7+ and 4.Nxe5.

338) 1.Qxg8! Rxg8 2.Nf6+ Ke7 3.Nxg8+ Ke8 4.Nf6+ Ke7 5.Nxd7 wins the exchange.

339) 1.Qxg6! fxg6 2.Nf7+ and 3.Nxd8.

340) 1.Rxf7+!! Kg8 [after 1...Kxf7 2.Ng5+! Qxg5 - or 2...Kg8 3.Qe6+ Kh8 4.Nf7+ and 5.Nxd8 - 3.Qe6+ Kf8 4.Qxe8#] **2.Ng5! Nf6** [2...Qxg5 3.Rxe8+ Kxf7 4.Qe6#] **3.Rxg7+ Kxg7 4.Ne6+** and 5.Nxd8.

341) 1.Qf6! Qxf6 2.Nxf6 Nf3 3.Rf4 Nd2+ 4.Ka2 Nxb3 5.Kxb3 Rh8 6.Nd7+ picking up the exchange.

342) 1...Bxe3 2.fxe3 Nc2 3.Rg1 Nxe3+ and 4...Nxd1.

343) 1.b5+! and wins, since if 1...Kxb6 2.Nd7+ and 3.Nxf8 or 1...Kxc5 2.Nd7+ again, finally on 1...Kc7 2.Ne6+ wins.

344) 1.Rxf8!! Qxf8 2.Rd8! Qxd8 [if the Queen moves off of the back rank then 3.Rh8#] **3.Nxf7+ and 4.Nxd8.**

345) 1...Ngf3+! 2.gxf3 Bh4! 3.Qg2 [on 3.Qxh4 comes the fork 3...Nxf3+] **3...Bxe1** winning the exchange.

346) 1.Nf6+! gxf6 2.Qg3+ Bg7 [2..Kh8 3.Bxf6+] **3.Bxf6** and mate after Qxg7.

347) 1.Nf6+! Bxf6 2.Qxg6+ Kh8 3.Qh7#.

348) 1.Rxc6+ Qxc6 2.Ne7+ and 3.Nxc6.

349) 1.Nxf6+ gxf6 2.Rxd4+ wins.

350) 1.Nf7+ Kg8 [1...Rxf7 2.Qc8+ Bd8 3.Qxd8+ Rf8 4.Qxf8#] **2.Nh6+ Kh8 3.Qxg7+! Kxg7 4.Nxf5+** and 5.Nxe3.

351) 1.b4 Bb6 2.b5 Na5 3.Ne7+.

352) 1.Nxc6 Bxc6 2.Ne7+ K moves 3.Nxc6 wins a pawn plus the exchange.

353) 1.Qxc8 Rxc8 2.Nd7+ K moves 3.Nxb6.

354) 1.Nd8+! Rxd8 2.Qxe7+ and 3.Qxd8.

355) 1...Qxe4 2.Nxe4 Ne2+.

356) 1.Nd5+! The Black c-pawn is pinned.

357) 1.Rh5+! Kf6 [forced, since 1..Bxh5 allows 2.Ne6+ and 3.Nxc7] **2.Rxf5+** followed by 3.Kxg4.

358) 1.Nb6+ cxb6 2.Be6.

359) 1.Nb5+ Kb8 2.Qa7+ Kc8 3.Nd6+ and 4.Nxf7.

360) 1.Qxd4! cxd4 2.Nxf6+ Kh8 3.Rxe8+ Rxe8 4.Bg7+!! Kxg7 5.Nxe8+ **K-moves 6.Nxc7** winning a piece.

361) 1...Nf3+ 2.Kd1 [after 2.Kf1 the same move wins while 2.Ke2 loses the Bishop to 2...Nd4+] **2...e2+ 3.Kxe2 Nd4+** and 4...Nxf5

362) 1.Rxh4! Qxh4 2.Qxf8+! Kxf8 3.Ng6+ and 4.Nxh4.

363) 1...Bxf3+! 2.Bxf3 Rh2+ 3.Kxh2 Nxf3+ and **4...Nxd4** wins a pawn.

364) 1.Qxb7 Bxb7 2.Rxd8 Rxd8 3.Nf7+ Kg8 4.Nxd8.

365) 1...Qxc1 !! 2.Qxc1 Rxc3 ! 3.Qe1 [3.Qxc3 Ne2+] 3...Rc1 ! 4.Qc1 Ne2+ wins a piece.

366) 1.Nd6 Bd7 [otherwise 2.Nf5+] **2.Re7+ Kf6 3.Rxd7 Ke6 4.Rd8 Ke7 5.Nf5+** and 6.Nxd4.

367) 1.Nd5 ! Qxf5 [1...cxd5 allows 2.Qc7+ Ka8 3.Qxb7#] **2.Rxb7+ Kxb7 3.Qb4+ Kc8** [3...Ka8 4.Nc7#] **4.Ne7+** and 5.Nxf5.

368) 1...Nxd4 2.Nxc7 Ne2+ 3.Kh1 Nxc1.

369) 1.Rxf8+ Rxf8 2.Rxf8+ Qxf8 3.Nxg6+ and 4.Nxf8.

370) 1.N[either] d6+ Bxd6 2.Nxd6+ Kb8 3.Nxf7.

371) 1.Bxf8 Kxf8 2.Bxf7 Kxf7 3.Nd6+ and 4.Nxc8.

372) 1. Nd6+ Kf8 2.Nxb7.

373) 1...Bxe4 !! 2.fxe4 [if 2.Nxd6, then 2...Bd3!] **2...Nxe4 3.Qe1 Ng3+ ! 4.Kg**1 [4.hxg3 hxg3 winning] **4...Nh3+ ! 5.gxh3 Ne2+ 6.Kh1 Qg1#.**

374) 1.Ne4 !! Be8 [1...Rxh5 2.Rxd7+!] **2.Bg5 !** and wins.

375) 1.Bxe6+ !! and wins! [if 1...Bxe6 2.Qf8+! 2.Kxf8 3.Nxe6+ Ke7 4.Nxc7 Kd6 5.Ne8+]. Beautiful play by Seirawan.

376) 1.Qxc6 Qxc6 2.Nxe7+ Kh8 3.Nxc6 winning.

6. DOUBLE ATTACK

As the name implies, the double attack is a simultaneous attack on two enemy pieces. It should be noted that the Knight fork is a particularly noted form of the double attack. Due to the intrinsic peculiarity of the Knight's move (it is the only piece which can "jump" over other pieces) and its fascinating symbolic impression-largely from its association with medieval horsemen-it has become traditional to consider the Knight fork as a separate tactical motif. Every piece can potentially double attack enemy units, even the lowly pawn is often involved. Very impressive is the long range striking power of the Queen in double attack situations, although the Rook and (more rarely) the Bishop can offer fine examples.

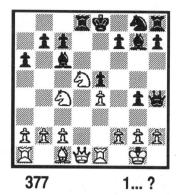

377　　　　1... ?

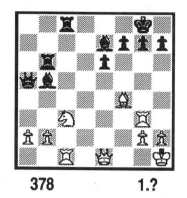

378　　　　1.?

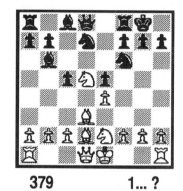

379　　　　1... ?

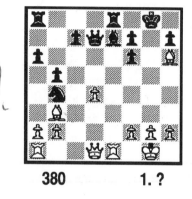

380　　　　1. ?

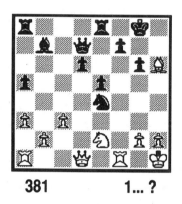

381　　　　1... ?

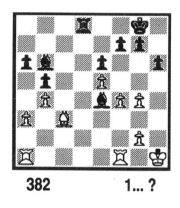

382　　　　1... ?

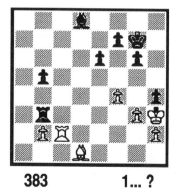

383　　　　1... ?

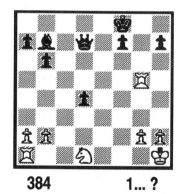

384　　　　1... ?

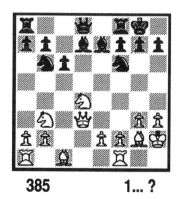

385　　　　1... ?

DOUBLE ATTACK

80

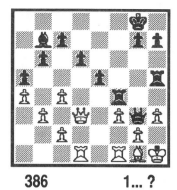

386   1... ?

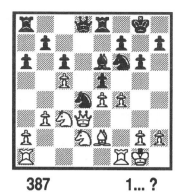

387   1... ?

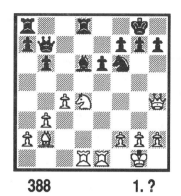

388   1. ?

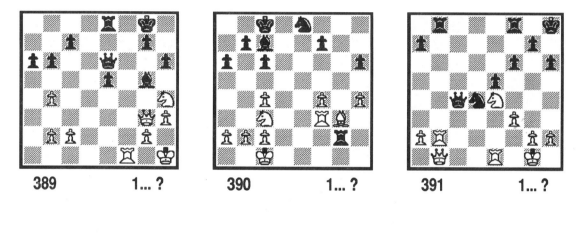

389   1... ?

390   1... ?

391   1... ?

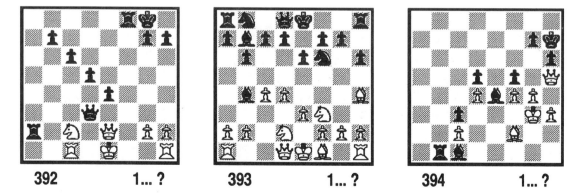

392   1... ?

393   1... ?

394   1... ?

DOUBLE ATTACK

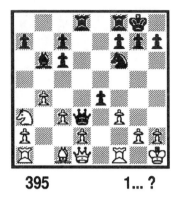

395   1... ?

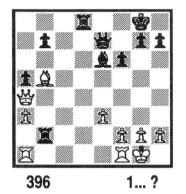

396   1... ?

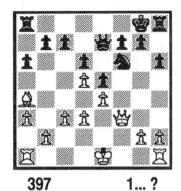

397   1... ?

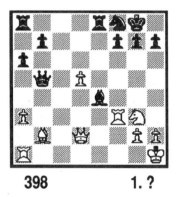

398   1. ?

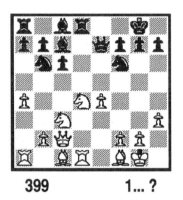

399   1... ?

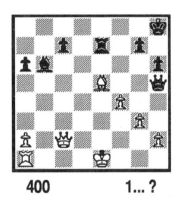

400   1... ?

401   1... ?   402   1... ?   403   1... ?

DOUBLE ATTACK

404   1... ?

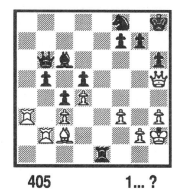

405   1... ?

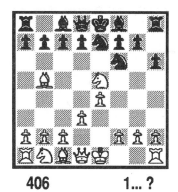

406   1... ?

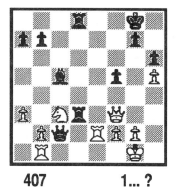

407   1... ?

408   1... ?

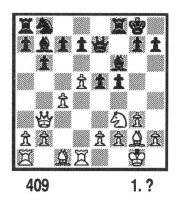

409   1. ?

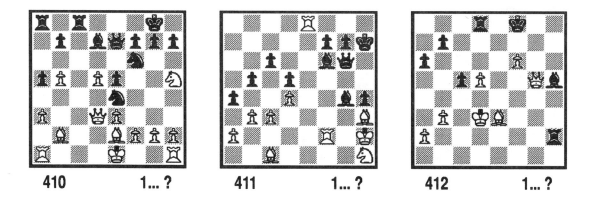

410   1... ?

411   1... ?

412   1... ?

DOUBLE ATTACK

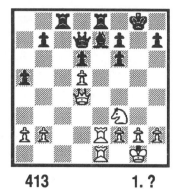

413 1. ?

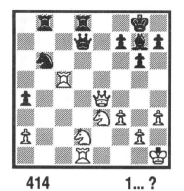

414 1... ?

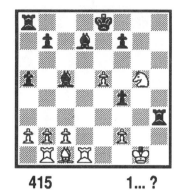

415 1... ?

416 1... ?

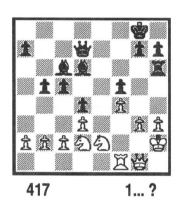

417 1... ?

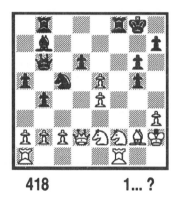

418 1... ?

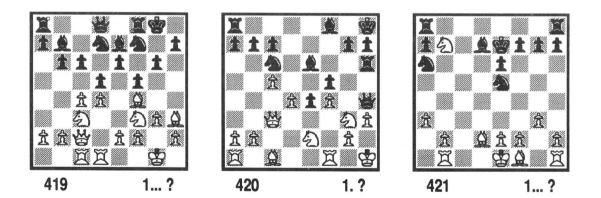

419 1... ?

420 1. ?

421 1... ?

DOUBLE ATTACK

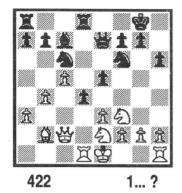

422   1... ?

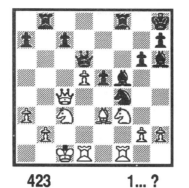

423   1... ?

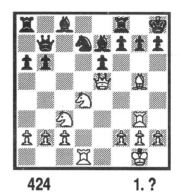

424   1. ?

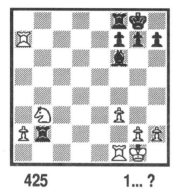

425   1... ?

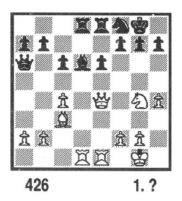

426   1. ?

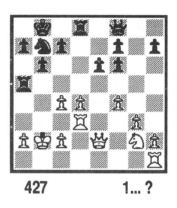

427   1... ?

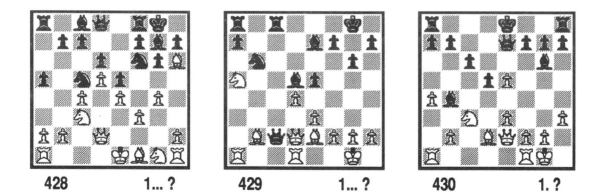

428   1... ?

429   1... ?

430   1. ?

DOUBLE ATTACK

85

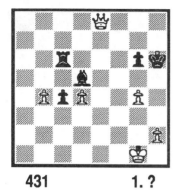

431   1. ?

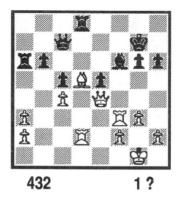

432   1 ?

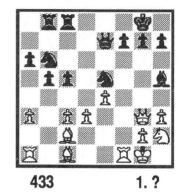

433   1. ?

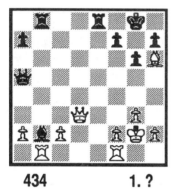

434   1. ?

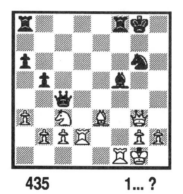

435   1... ?

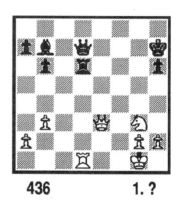

436   1. ?

437   1. ?

438   1. ?

439   1. ?

DOUBLE ATTACK

86

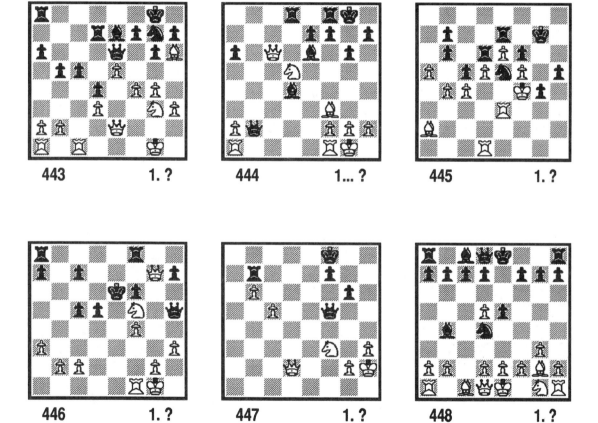

| 440 | 1. ? | 441 | 1... ? | 442 | 1. ? |

| 443 | 1. ? | 444 | 1... ? | 445 | 1. ? |

| 446 | 1. ? | 447 | 1. ? | 448 | 1. ? |

DOUBLE ATTACK

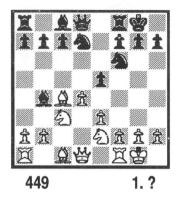

449   1. ?

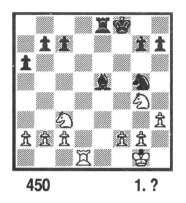

450   1. ?

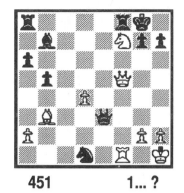

451   1... ?

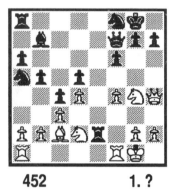

452   1. ?

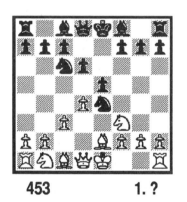

453   1. ?

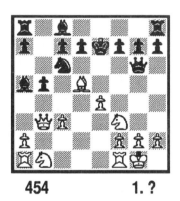

454   1. ?

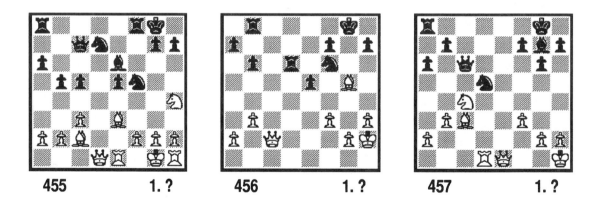

455   1. ?

456   1. ?

457   1. ?

DOUBLE ATTACK

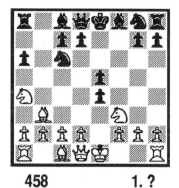

458   1. ?

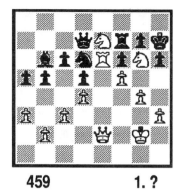

459   1. ?

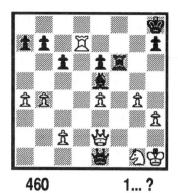

460   1... ?

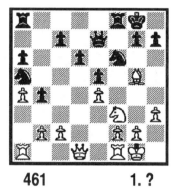

461   1. ?

462   1... ?

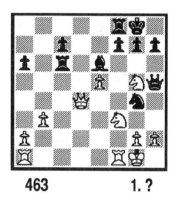

463   1. ?

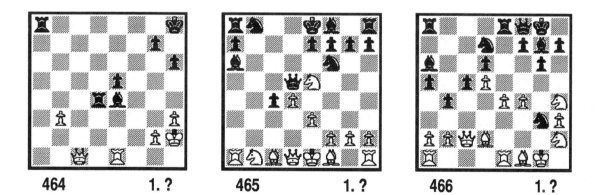

464   1. ?

465   1. ?

466   1. ?

DOUBLE ATTACK

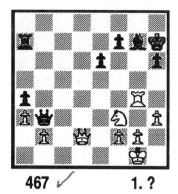

467 ✓   1. ?

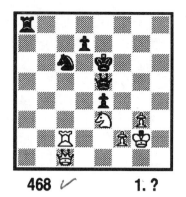

468 ✓   1. ?

469 ⌐   1.... ?

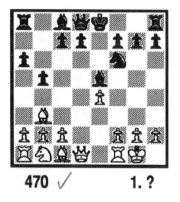

470 ✓   1. ?

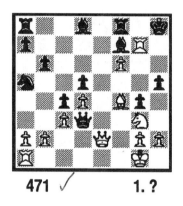

471 ✓   1. ?

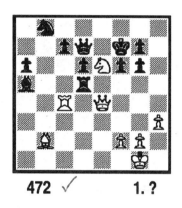

472 ✓   1. ?

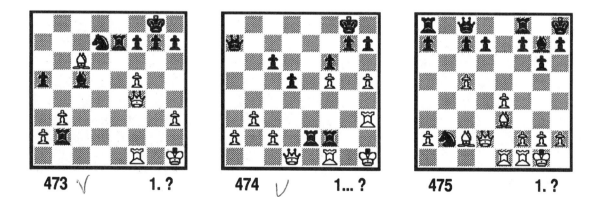

473 ✓   1. ?

474 ∨   1... ?

475   1. ?

DOUBLE ATTACK

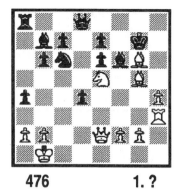

476   1. ?

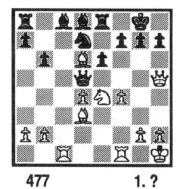

477   1. ?

478   1. ?

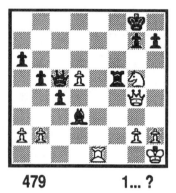

479   1... ?

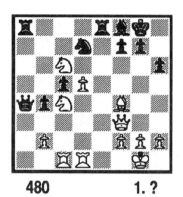

480   1. ?

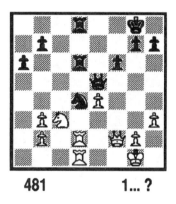

481   1... ?

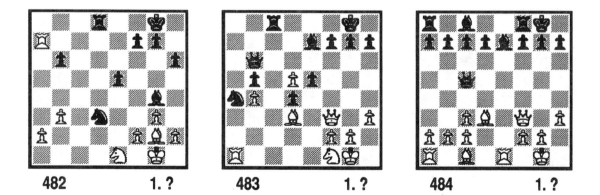

482   1. ?
     483   1. ?
     484   1. ?

DOUBLE ATTACK

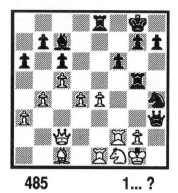

485   1... ?

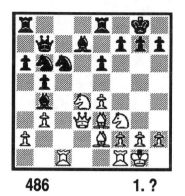

486   1. ?

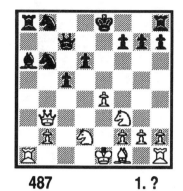

487   1. ?

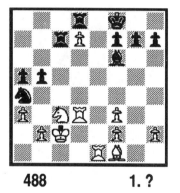

488   1. ?

489   1. ?

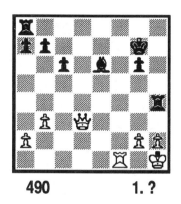

490   1. ?

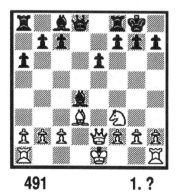

491   1. ?

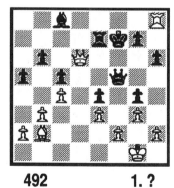

492   1. ?

493   1... ?

DOUBLE ATTACK

377) 1...Bxd5! 2.exd5 g3! 3.hxg3 Qxc4 wins a piece.

378) 1.Bc7 Rxc7 2.Qe5! wins the exchange.

379) 1...Nxd5 2.exd5 c4! 3.Bxc4 [on 3.Bf5 Qf6 or 3.Be4 f5] **3...Qh4!**

380) 1.Rxe7! Rxe7 2.Qf3! picks up the Ra8.

381) 1...Qh3!! [threatening both 2...Qxh6 and 2...Ng3+] **2.gxh3 Nf2+ 3.Kg1 Nxh3#.**

382) 1...Rd3! winning the Bc3 since mate by 2...Rh3 is also threatened.

383) 1...hxg3 [at first sight a blunder] **2.Rd2** [attacking both d8 and b3] **2...gxh2+ 3.Kxh2** [if 3.Kg2 then 3...Rh3! since 4.Kxh3 allows 4...h1=Q+] **3...Bc7!** The point. Now 4.Bxb3 is answered by 4...Bxf4+ and 5...Bxd2.

384) 1...Qe7! [threatening both 2...Qxg5 and 2...Qe1#] **2.h4 Qe1+ 3. Kh2 Qxh4+** and 4...Qxg5.

385) 1...c5 2.Nf3 c4 wins a piece.

386) 1...Rxf3! 2.Bh2 [not 2.gxf3 Rxh3+ and mate next. Also bad is 2.Rxf3 Rxh3+! 3.gxh3 Bxf3+] **2...Rxh3! 3.gxh3 Rxf1#.**

387) 1...Nxe2+ 2.Qxe2 Qd4+.

388) 1.Nxe6! fxe6 2.Bxf6 gxf6 3.Rxd6! Rxd6 4.Qg3+ and **5.Qxd6.**

389) 1...Qc4! winning either the Rf1 or the Nh4.

390) 1...Rxg3! 2.Rxg3 Bxf4+ and 3...Bxg3.

391) 1...Nxf3+! 2.gxf3 Qd4+ 3.Kh1 Rxb2.

392) 1...d4 [threat: 2...Qe2+ 3.Kxe2 d3+] **2.Qxd3 exd3 3.N moves d2+** and 4...dxc1=Q winning.

393) 1...g5! 2.Bg3 g4 3.a3 [if the Nf3 moves then 3...Ne4! pins and wins the Nd2] **3...gxf3 4.axb4 fxg2** winning a piece.

394) 1...g6 2.Qh4 Bxf4+! 3.Kxf4 g5+.

395) 1...e3 [threatening 2...e2] **2.Re1 exd2** wins a piece.

396) 1...Rd5! 2.Bc4 b5!

397) 1...Nxd5! 2.exd5 Qh4+ and 3...Qxa4.

398) 1.Qd4 f6 2.Ne4 Rxe4 3.Qxe4 Qxb2 and White has won the exchange.

399) 1...Rxd4! 2.Rxd4 Qe5! threatening mate and the Rd4.

400) 1...Rxe5+! 2.fxe5 Qxe5+ and Qxa1.

401) 1...Bxg2+! 2.Kxg2 Qg4+ 3.Kf1 [3.Kh1 Qf3#] 3...Qxd1+ 4.Kg2 Qg4+ 5.Kf1 Qf3+ 6.Ke1 Qxe4+ 7.Kf1 Qf3+ 8.Ke1 Bxg1.

402) 1...Bxc3! 2.bxc3 Nxe3 3.fxe3 Qxe3+ and 4...Qxd3.

403) 1...Qe1+ 2.Rd1 Qe4! [threatening mate] **3.Rd3 Qh1+ 4.Rd1 Qxh2** threatening mate again and thereby picking up still another pawn with an easy win.

404) 1...Bxh2+! 2.Kxh2 Nxf2 3.Qe2 Nxd3 4.Qxd3 Bxf3 5.Qxf3 Qh4+ and 6...Qxe1.

405) 1...Qc7+! 2.g3 Qe7! and wins because of the double threat of 3...Qe2# and 3...Qxa3.

406) 1...c6! 2.Bc4 Qa5+ wins the Ne5.

407) 1...Qxb1+ 2.Nxb1 Rxf3 3.gxf3 Rd1+ and 4...Rxb1.

408) 1...Bxe4 2.fxe4 Rxh3! 3.gxh3 Qxe4+ and 4...Qxb1.

409) 1.Nh4! Bxh4 2.d6! cd 3.Bxb7 Nc6 4.Bxa8 Rxa8 5.gxh4 winning a rook.

410) 1...Nxf2 2.Kxf2 Nxh5 3.Bxh5 Qh4+ and 4...Qxh5.

411) 1...Bxh3 2.Kxh3 Qg1 winning a piece.

412) 1...Rxd5+! 2.Qxd5 Bg6+ 3.Qe4 [on 3.Kc4 or 3.Kc3 Black mates with 3...Rc2] **3...Bxe4+** winning.

413) 1.Rxe7 Rxe7 2.Rxe7 Qxe7 3.Qg4+ and 4.Qxc8.

414) 1...Re8 2.Qf4 Qd4! wins by the attack on both c5 and e3 after 3.Qxd4 Bxd4.

415) 1...Rg3+.

416) 1...Qc6! attacking both Ba6 and Rh1.

417) 1...Qe6 2.Qf2 Rxh3+! 3.Kxh3 Qh6#.

418) 1...Rxf2! 2.Rxf2 Nxe4 3.Bxe4 Qxf2+ and mate next.

419) 1...g5 2.Be3 g4.

420) 1.d5! Bxd5 2.Nxf5 and 3.Nxh6.

421) 1...Bc6 spearing both the Nb7 and Rh1.

422) 1...d3! 2.Rxd3 Rxd3 3.Qxd3 e4 wins a piece.

423) 1...Qb6!! [threatening both mate at b2 and the Be3] **2.Bxb6 Ne2#!**

424) 1.Bh6! Nxe5 2.Bxg7+ Kg8 3.Bxe5+ Bg5 4.Rxg5#.

425) 1...Rxb3! 2.axb3 Bd4+.

426) 1.Rxd6! Rxd6 2.Qe5 winning the Rd6 due to the mate threat.

427) 1...Rxd4! 2.Rxd4 Qa3+ 3.Kb1 Qxa2+ 4.Kc1 Qa1+ and 5...Qxd4.

428) 1...Nfxe4 2.Nxe4 Nxe4 3.fxe4 Qh4+ and wins the Bh6 remaining a pawn ahead.

429) 1...Qxd2 2.Rxd2 Bb4 3.Rd1 Rc2.

430) 1.Nxd5! cxd5 2.Qb5+ and 3.Qxb4.

431) 1.Qh8+ Kg5 2.Qe5+ and 3.Qxd5.

432) 1.Bf7!! Kxf7 [if 1...Rxd2 then White has 2.Qxg6+ Kf8 3.Qg8+ Ke7 4.Qe8+ Kd6 5.Qe6#, or if 1...Qxf7 then 2.Rxd8 wins the exchange] **2.Rxd8 Qxd8 3.Qb7+ and 4.Qxa6.**

433) 1.Rf5 wins either the Ne5 or Bh5.

434) 1.Rxb2! Rxb2 2.Qd4 Qe5 3.Re1! Qxe1 [or 3...Qxd4 4.Rxe8#] **4.Qg7#.**

435) 1...Qxf1+ 2.Kxf1 Bd3+ 3.Ke1 Rf1#.

436) 1.Qxh6+!! Kxh6 [1...Rxh6 2.Rxd7+] **2.Rxd6+ Qxd6 3.Nf5+** and 4.Nxd6.

437) 1.Nxe5 Qxe5 2.Bxd6+.

438) 1.Ne8! Qe7 2.Qg3 Qxe8 3.Qxb8.

439) 1.Rxg7! Kxg7 [or 1...Qxg7 2.Bf6] **2.Bxf6+! Qxf6 3.Nh5+** wins the Queen.

440) 1.d7 Rd8 2.Qa5 wins, since 2...Rb8 fails to 3.d8=Q+.

441) 1...Rxd4! 2.Rxd4 Ne4!! 3.Rxe4 [3.Qe7 Nf2+ 4.Kg1 Qxg2#] **3...Bxg5 4.fxg5 b4!** and wins.

442) 1.f3 Qh4 2.Qxh4 gxh4 3.e4.

443) 1.Bxg7 Kxg7 2.f5 gxf5 3.gxf5 Qc6 4.f6+ wins a piece.

444) 1...Bxd5! 2.Bxd5 Qb5! 3.Qxb5 axb5 4.Bc6 Bxa1.

445) 1.Rxe5 fxe5+ 2.Kxe5 and the duel threats of 3.Kxd6 and 3.f6+ win.

446) 1.Qe7+ Kxf5 2.g4+.

447) 1.c6 Rxb6 [1...Rb8 2.Qd6+] **2.Qd8+ and 3.Qxb6.**

448) 1.e3 Nf5 [1...Nb5 2.Qa4!] **2.Qg4!** wins either the Nf5 or Bb4.

449) 1.Bxf7+! Rxf7 [Kxf7 2.Qb3+] **2.dxe5 Ng4 3.e6** winning back the piece with an extra pawn to boot.

450) 1.Nxe5 Rxe5 2.f4.

451) 1...Bxg2+! 2.Kxg2 Qxb3! 2.axb3 Ne3+ 4.K moves Nxf5 and 5...Rxf7 wins.

452) 1.Nh6+! gxh6 2.Qg4+ and 3.Qxe2.

453) 1.d5 Ne7 2.Qa4+!

454) 1.Bxc6 dxc6 [1...Qxc6 makes no difference] **2.Qa3+** and 3.Qxa5.

455) 1.Nxf5 Bxf5 2.Bxf5 Rxf5 3.Qd5+ and 4.Qxa8.

456) 1.Qc7 Rbd8 2.Bxf6 wins, since 2...Rxf6 allows 3.Qxd8+.

457) 1.Bxg7 Kxg7 [if 1...Re8 then 2.Be5! f6 3.Qe4! keeps the extra piece] **2.Qe5+ Nf6 3.Rd6!**

458) 1.Nxe5! Nxe5 2.Qh5+ Ng6 3.Qd5 threatening both 4.Qf7# and 4.Qxa8.

459) 1.Nxd5! cxd5 2.Rxd6! Qxd6 3.Qe8! [threatening mate at h8] **3...Rf8 4.Nxf8+ Qxf8** [4...Kh8 5.Ng6+ and mate next] **5.Qxf8 wins.**

460) 1...Rf2!! and wins. [2.Qxe1 Rh2#].

461) 1. Bxf6 Qxf6 2.Qd5+.

462) 1...Qb4+! 2.Kd1 Bd3! 3.Qxd3 Nxf2+ and 4...Nxd3.

463) 1.h3! Nh6 2.Qe4 threatening both 3.Qxc6 and 3.Qxh7#.

464) **1.Rxe4! Rxe4 2.Qc6** wins a Rook.

465) **1.Rxa6 Nxa6 2.Qa4+** and 3.Qxa6 wins two pieces for the Rook.

466) **1.Bxa6 Rxa6 2.Qd3** attacks both the Ra6 and Ng3.

467) **1.Rxg7+ Kxg7 2.Qd4+** and 3.Qxa7.

468) **1. Rxc6+ dxc6 2.Qxc6+** and 3.Qxa8.

469) **1...Rxc3! 2.Rxc3 Rxa2+! 3.Kb3** [3.Kxa2 Nc3+] **3...Rxe2** with a won ending.

470) **1.f4 Bd6 2.e5 Bc5+ 3.Kh1 Ng8 4.Qd5** threatening 5.Qf7#, 5.Qxc5 and 5.Qxa8.

471) **1.Rxf7! Rxf7** [1...Qxe2 2.Rxf8+] **2.Qe8+ Kh7 3.Qxf7+ and 4.Qg7#.**

472) **1.Nd8+!** [1.Qd5 Qxe6 2.Qxe6+ Kxe6 leaves Black with too many pawns for the exchange] **1...Qxd8 2.Qxd5+ Kf8 3.Qxa5.**

473) **1.f6! gxf6** [1...Nxf6 2.Qb8+] **2.Bxd7 Rxd7 3.Qg4+** and 4.Qxd7.

474) **1...Qe3!** and Black wins. [2.Rxe3 Rh2+ 3.Kg1 Reg2#, or 2.Rxf2 Qxh3+].

475) **1.Bd4 Rg8** [1..Nc4 2.Bxg7+ Kxg7 3.Qd4+ and 4.Qxc4] **2.Bxg7+ Rxg7 3.Qd4 Rb8 4.Rb1 Qb7 5.Bb3!** and the Knight is lost.

476) **1.Bh6+! Kg8** [on 1...Kxh6 then 2.Qh5+ Kg7 3.Qh7+ Kf8 4.Qf7#] **2.Nxc6 Bxc6 3.Qxe6+** and 4.Qxc6.

477) **1.Ng5 Nf6** [1...Bxg5 2.Qxh7# or 1...Qxd6 then 2.Bxh7+ Kh8 3.Nxf7#] **2.Bxh7+ Kh8 3.Nxf7#.**

478) **1.Rxf7! Rxf7 2.Bxf7+ Kxf7 3.Qc4+** wins a Bishop with an extra pawn netted.

479) **1...Qe3!** winning. [2.Rxe3 Rf1#; 2.Ra1 Qxg5].

480) **1.Bxh6! gxh6 2.Qg4+.**

481) **1...Nf3+!** winning. [2.gxf3 Qg5+].

482) **1.Nxd3 Rxd3 2.Ra8+ Kh7 3.Be4+.**

483) **1.Qf5** wins, threatening both 2.Qxc8 and mate by 2.Qxh7+ and 3.Qh8.

484) **1.Qe4!**

485) **1...Rxg2!+ 2.Rxg2 Nf3+ 3.Kf2 Qg2+! 4.Kxg2 Nxe1+** and wins.

486) **1.Nxc6 Bxc6 2.Qd4 Ba5 3.b4 Red8 4.Qc5** wins the Ba5.

487) **1.Bxa6 Rxa6 2.Rxa6 Nxa6 3.Qb5+** and 4.Qxa6.

488) **1.Re8+! Rxe8 2.dxe8=Q+ Kxe8 3.Re3+! Kd8** [or 3...Kf8 4.Bxb5 threatens both 5.Re8# and 5.Bxa4, while 3....Kd7 loses to 4.Bxb5+] **4.Bxb5** and wins the Na4 since 5.Re8# is also threatened.

489) **1.Qd4!** threatens 2.Qg7# and 2.Qxe3.

490) **1.Qc3+ K moves 2.Qe1!** wins the Be6 or Rh4.

491) **1.Qe4!**

492) **1.Qd8!** threatening 2.Qxc8 as well as 2.Rf8+.

493) **1...Rg2!!** winning. [Threat of 2...Nf4#] **2.Kxg2 Ne3+** and 3...Nxd1.

100

7. DISCOVERY

The discovery is one of the most powerful types of move possible in a game of chess. The term "discovery" simply means that a piece is moved from a rank, file, or diagonal while uncovering an attack by friendly forces behind it on the line, thereby giving both pieces a chance to simultaneously threaten the opponent. Discoveries come in three varieties. The most powerful is the DOUBLE CHECK, in which the moving piece gives check and uncovers a check on the enemy King by another piece. It is easy to analyze the response to double check: The attacked King must move. Interposition or capture of a checking piece are not possible. DISCOVERED CHECK means that the enemy King is attacked only by the piece unleashed along the line (file, rank, or diagonal), while the moving or discovering piece is free to make threats of its own. DISCOVERED ATTACK occurs in the same manner as the others, except that the enemy King is not directly involved. Discovered attacks of any kind are extremely dangerous and even the threat of a discovered check or double check often brings a chess game to a sudden end. Watch for all three types of discovery in this chapter.

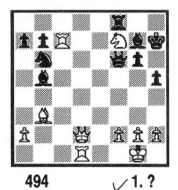

494   ✓ 1. ?

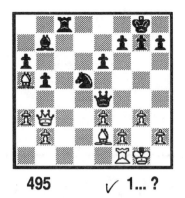

495   ✓ 1... ?

496   ✓ 1. ?

497   ✓ 1... ?

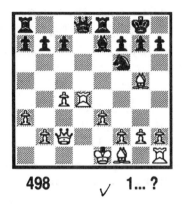

498   ✓ 1... ?

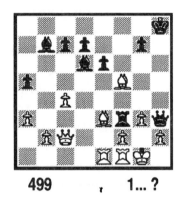

499   , 1... ?

500   ✓ 1... ?

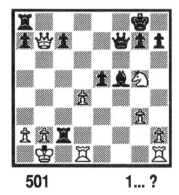

501   1... ?

502   1... ?

DISCOVERY

503   , 1. ?

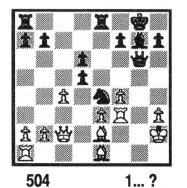

504   1... ?

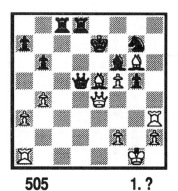

505   1. ?

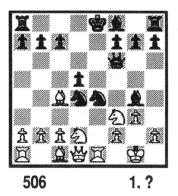

506   1. ?

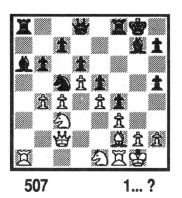

507   1... ?

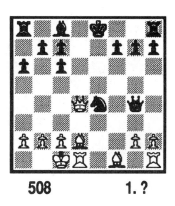

508   1. ?

509   1. ?

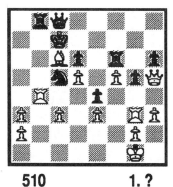

510   1. ?

511   1. ?

DISCOVERY

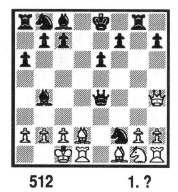

512   1. ?

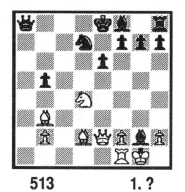

513   1. ?

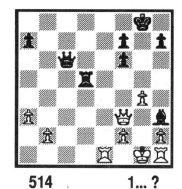

514   1... ?

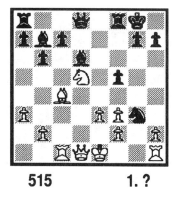

515   1. ?

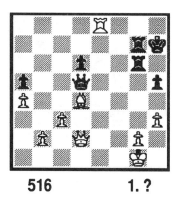

516   1. ?

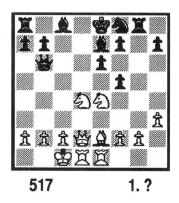

517   1. ?

518   1. ?

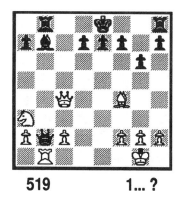

519   1... ?

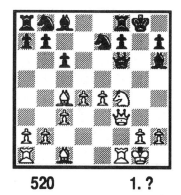

520   1. ?

DISCOVERY

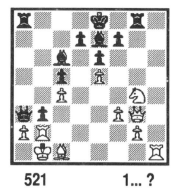

521   1... ?

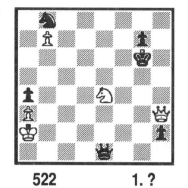

522   1. ?

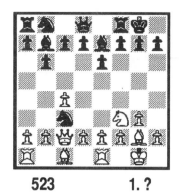

523   1. ?

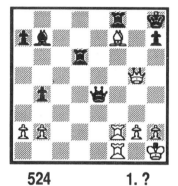

524   1. ?

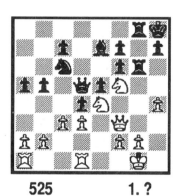

525   1. ?

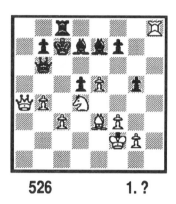

526   1. ?

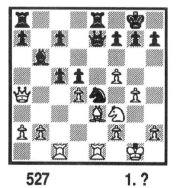

527   1. ?

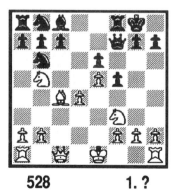

528   1. ?

529   1... ?

DISCOVERY

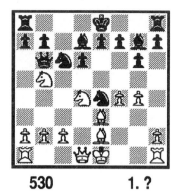

530   1. ?

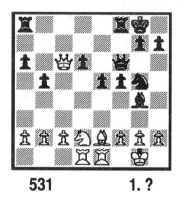

531   1. ?

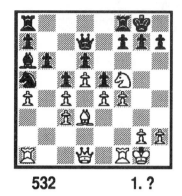

532   1. ?

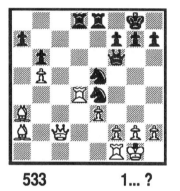

533   1... ?

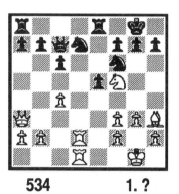

534   1. ?

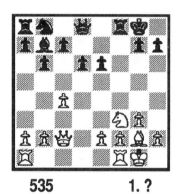

535   1. ?

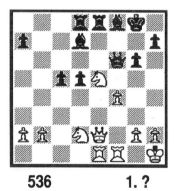

536   1. ?

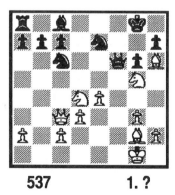

537   1. ?

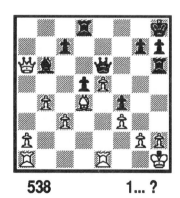

538   1... ?

DISCOVERY

539   1. ?

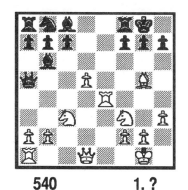

540   1. ?

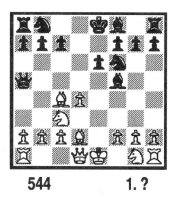

541   1. ?

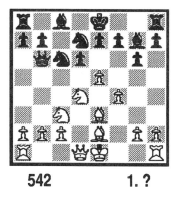

542   1. ?

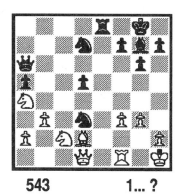

543   1... ?

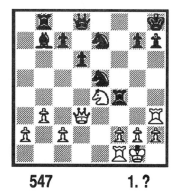

544   1. ?

545   1. ?

546   1. ?

547   1. ?

DISCOVERY

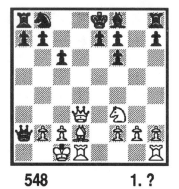

548   1. ?

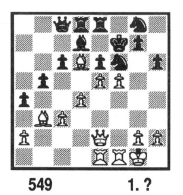

549   1. ?

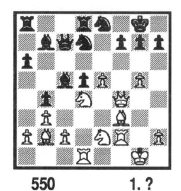

550   1. ?

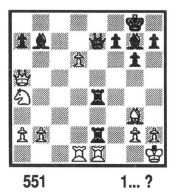

551   1... ?

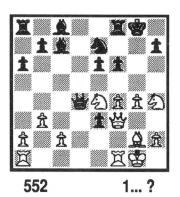

552   1... ?

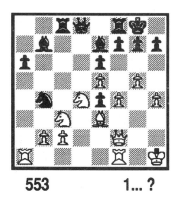

553   1... ?

554   1... ?

555   1... ?

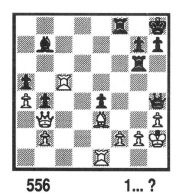

556   1... ?

DISCOVERY

557　　　　　　1... ?

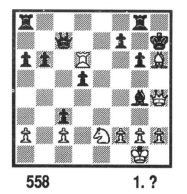

558　　　　　　1. ?

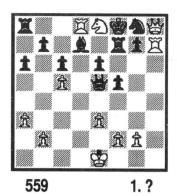

559　　　　　　1. ?

560　　　　　　1. ?

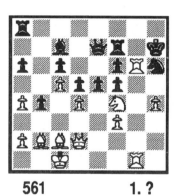

561　　　　　　1. ?

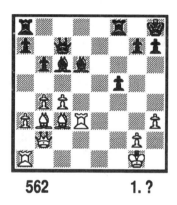

562　　　　　　1. ?

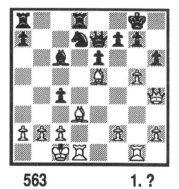

563　　　　　　1. ?

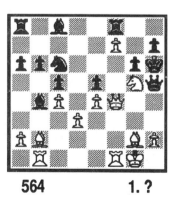

564　　　　　　1. ?

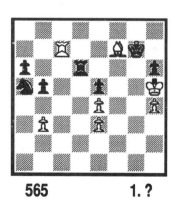

565　　　　　　1. ?

DISCOVERY

566   1. ?

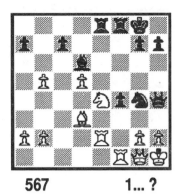

567   1... ?

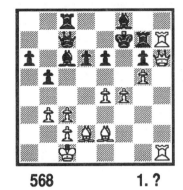

568   1. ?

569   1. ?

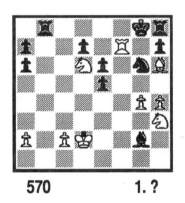

570   1. ?

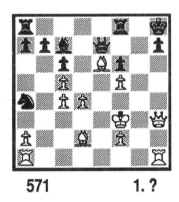

571   1. ?

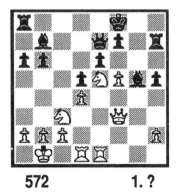

572   1. ?

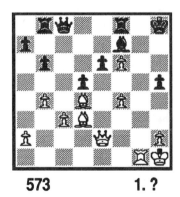

573   1. ?

574   1... ?

DISCOVERY

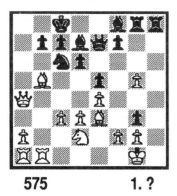

575   1. ?

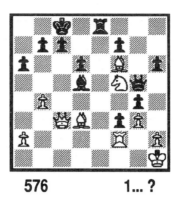

576   1... ?

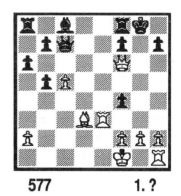

577   1. ?

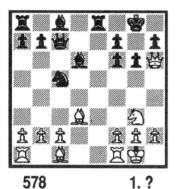

578   1. ?

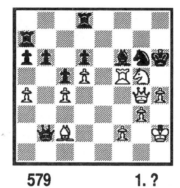

579   1. ?

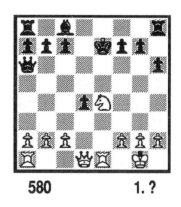

580   1. ?

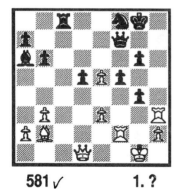

581 ✓   1. ?

582 ✓   1. ?

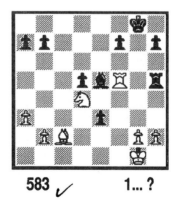

583 ✓   1... ?

DISCOVERY

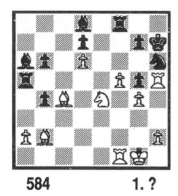

584   1. ?

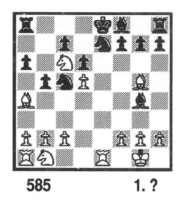

585   1. ?

586   1. ?

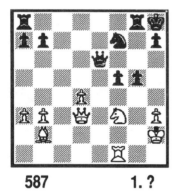

587   1. ?

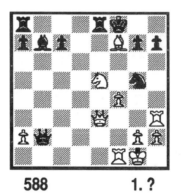

588   1. ?

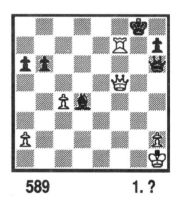

589   1. ?

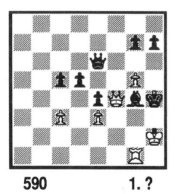

590   1. ?

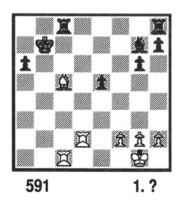

591   1. ?

592   1... ?

DISCOVERY

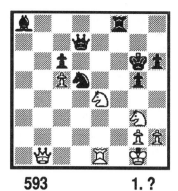

593   1. ?

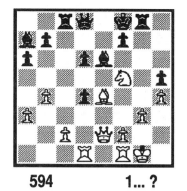

594   1... ?

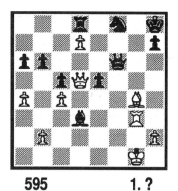

595   1. ?

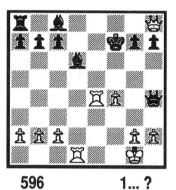

596   1... ?

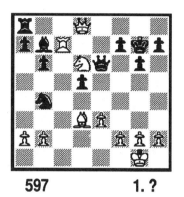

597   1. ?

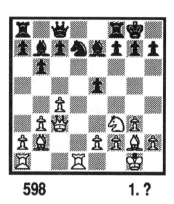

598   1. ?

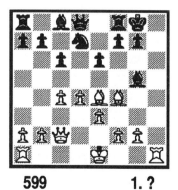

599   1. ?

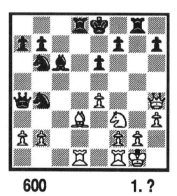

600   1. ?

601   1... ?

DISCOVERY

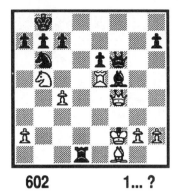

602   1... ?

603   1... ?

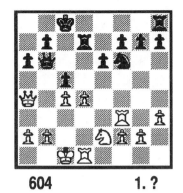

604   1. ?

605   1... ?

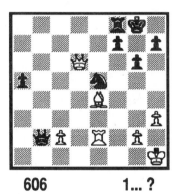

606   1... ?

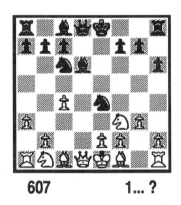

607   1... ?

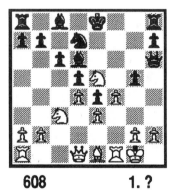

608   1. ?

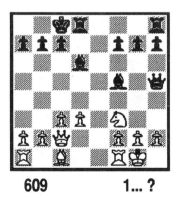

609   1... ?

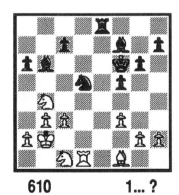

610   1... ?

DISCOVERY

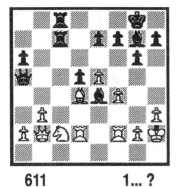

611   1... ?

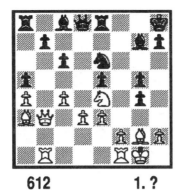

612   1. ?

613   1... ?

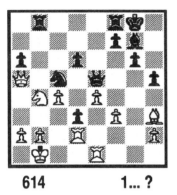

614   1... ?

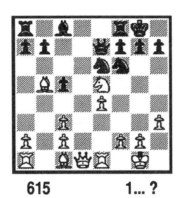

615   1... ?

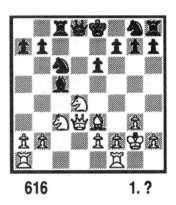

616   1. ?

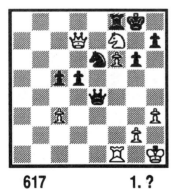

617   1. ?

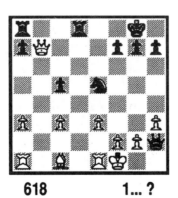

618   1... ?

619   1... ?

DISCOVERY

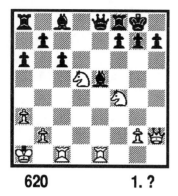

620   1. ?

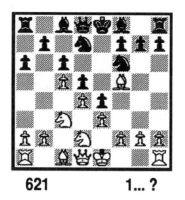

621   1... ?

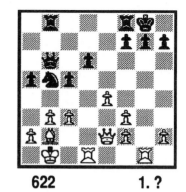

622   1. ?

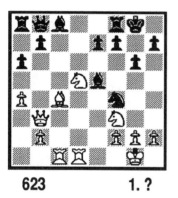

623   1. ?

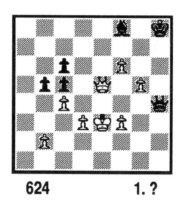

624   1. ?

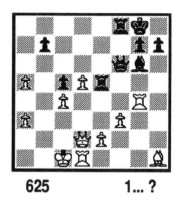

625   1... ?

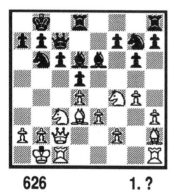

626   1. ?

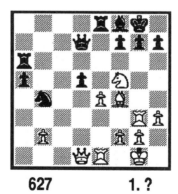

627   1. ?

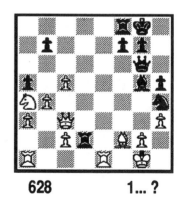

628   1... ?

DISCOVERY

494) 1.Qh6+! Bxh6 2.Ng5+ Kh8 3.Rh7#.

495) 1...Qg2+!! 2.Kxg2 Nf4+ 3. Kg1 Nh3#.

496) 1. Be6+ Kh8 [1...Kf8 2.Qh5! wins (2...Nxh5 3.Nxh7#)] **2.Nf7+ Kg8 3.Nxd6+ and 4.Nxc8 .**

497) 1...Rxf3! 2.Qxe2 Rxf1#.

498) 1...Qxd4 2.exd4 Bb4+ 3.Kd1 Re1#.

499) 1...Qg2+! 2.Kxg2 Rxg3+ and mate.

500) 1...Nf3#.

501) 1...Rc1+ 2.Kxc1 Qc4+ 3.Kd2 Qd3+ 4.Ke1 Qe3+ 5.Kf1 Rf8 and the coming discovered check by the Rf8 will be crushing.

502) 1...Bd3+ 2.Ke1 Rf1#.

503) 1.Qd7+! Bxd7 2.Nd6+ Kd8 3.Nf7+ Kc8 4.Re8+! Bxe8 5.Rd8#.

504) 1...Ng5! and wins [2.Qxg6 Nxf3+ 3.Bxf3 hxg6].

505) 1. Bd6+ Kxd6 2.Rd3 wins the Queen.

506) 1.Nxe4 Nxf3+ 2.Qxf3! Qxf3 3.Nf6+ Kd8 4.Re8#.

507) 1...Bxc4! winning. [1.Rxa8 Qxa8 2.bxc5 Qa6 and the Rf1 is lost].

508) 1.Qd8+!! Kxd8 2.Bg5+-+ Ke8 3.Rd8#.

509) 1.Rd7! Qxa1 2.Rxg7+! Kxg7 3.Bh6+ Kh8 4.Ng6+! hxg6 5.fxg6 Qf1+ 6.Kh4 Qf3 7.Bg7+ Kxg7 8.Qh7#.

510) 1.Rxg5! hxg5 2.Qh7+ Nd7 [or 2...Kd8 3.Qh8+ Ke7 4.Qg7+ Rf7 5.f6+] 3.Bxd7 Qg8 [on 3...Qxd7 4.Qxd7+ Kxd7 5.Rxb8] 4.Rb7+!! Kxb7 [4...Rxb7 5.Qxg8] 5.Bc8+!! Kxc8 6.Qxg8+.

511) 1.Qd8+! Kxd8 2.Bg5+ Ke8 [2...Kc7 3.Bd8#] 3.Rd8#.

512) 1.Qd8+ Kxd8 2.Bg5+ Ke8 3.Rd8#.

513) 1.Bxe6 Bxf1 [1...fxe6 2.Qxe6+ Be7 3.Re1 wins] 2.Bxf7+ Kd8 [2...Kxf7 3.Qe6#] 3.Qe8+ Kc7 4.Qxa8.

514) 1...Rd1!! and Black wins. [2.Qxc6 Rxe1#, or 2.Rxd1 Qxf3].

515) 1.Ne7+ Kh8 2.Ng6+ hxg6 3.hxg3+ Qh4 4.Rxh4#.

516) 1.Rh8+! Kxh8 2.Bxg7+ wins the Black Queen.

517) 1.Nxf5 exf5 2.Nf6+! Qxf6 3.Qd8+ Bxd8 4.Bb5#.

518) 1.Rxb7!! Qxe6 2.Bc5! Qxe2 [expecting 3.Rxe2, Rd1 and mate] 3.Rxe7+! Qxe7 4.Rxe7#.

519) 1...Qxb1+ 2.Nxb1 Ba6! and wins.

520) 1.Nd5 Nxd5 [1...Qxf3 2.Ne7+ wins a piece] 2.Qxf6 Nxf6 3.Bxh6 Nbd7 4.Bxf8 Kxf8 5.e5 Nd5 6.Bxd5 cxd5 7.e6 with an overwhelming position.

521) 1...Be4+!! wins. [2.Ka1 Qxa2+! 3.Rxa2 Rxa2#, or 2.fxe4 bxa2+ 3.Ka1 Qxg3].

522) 1.Qe6+ Kh7 [or 1...Kh5] **2.Nf6+ gxf6 3.Qxe1.**

523) 1.Ng5! Bxg5 2.Bxb7 Nxe2+ 3.Rxe2 and 4.Bxa8.

524) 1.Bd5!! [now, if 1...Qxd5 2.Rxf8+ mates, or 1...Rxd5 2.Rxf8#. Finally 1...Rxf2 2.Qg8#].

525) 1.Ng5! Rd8 [not 1...Qxf3 2.Nxf7#] **2.Qxd5 Rxd5 3.Nxf7+ Kg8 4.h5!** traps the Rg6 since 4...Rg4 allows 5.N(f7)h6+ and 6.Nxg4.

526) 1.Ne6+ Qxe6 2.Qa5+ Kb8 [2...Kc6 3.b5 is mate or 2...b6 3.Qa7+ Kc6 4.Qxb6#] **3.Ba7+ Ka8 4.Bb6+ Kb8 5.Qa7#.**

527) 1.dxc5 Bxc5 [1...Nxc5 2.Bxc5 wins as the Qe7 is attacked, too] **2.Bxc5 Nxc5 3.Rxc5! Qxc5 4.Rxe8+** and mate next.

528) 1.Nxc7 Qxc7 2.Bxe6+ and 3.Qxc7.

529) 1...Qxg5! 2.Qxg5 Bxe3+ wins. [3.Kb2 Rf2+; 3.Kd1 Rxf1+ 4.Rxf1 Bxg5].

530) 1.Ne6! Qa5+ [1...Qxe3 2.Nbc7#] **2.Bd2 Qxd2+ 3.Qxd2 Nxd2 4.Nbc7#.**

531) 1.f3 Bh5 2.f4! winning a piece after 2...Bxe2 3.fxg5 Qxg5 4.Rxe2 or 2...exf4 3.Bxh5.

532) 1.Qg4! g6 2.Nh6+ wins the Black Queen.

533) 1...Nf3+ 2.gxf3 Qg6+ 3.Kh1 Ng3+ picking up the White Queen.

534) 1.Rxd7 Nxd7 2.Rxd7 Qxd7 3.Nh6+ and 4.Bxd7.

535) 1.Ng5 Qxg5 2.Bxb7.

536) **1.Nxd7** and wins, since 1...Rxe2 is met by 2.Nxf6+ and 1...Rxd7 fails to 2.Qxe8.

537) **1.Nxc6 Qxc3** [1...Qxc6 2.Qg7#] **2.Nxe7+ Kh8 3.Nf7#.**

538) **1...Rxh2+ 2.Kxh2 Qh6+ 3.Kg1 Bxd4+** and the White Queen falls.

539) **1.Qxf8 Qxf8 2.c8=Q+** and wins.

540) **1.Be7! Re8 2.Bb4** attacking both the Queen and mate at e8.

541) **1.Rxe6+!** and now if 1..Bxe6 2.Bb5+ axb5 3.Qxd4 and 1...fxe6 loses to 2.Bg6+ and 3.Qxd4.

542) **1.Ne6!! Qxe3 2.Nd5! Qe4 3.Ndc7#.**

543) **1...Re1! 2.Bxe1** [2.Rxe1 Nf2+] **2...Nb2! 3.Bc3 Nxd1 4.Rxd1 Qe2.**

544) **1.Nd5! Qa4** [the only move] **2.Bb5+! Qxb5 3.Nxc7+ and 4.Nxb5.**

545) **1.Nxe5! Bxd1 2.Bxf7+ Ke7 3.Nd5#.**

546) **1.d5!** and wins the Nb6.

547) **1.Nf6!!** winning, as 1...Nxd3 is met by 2.Rxh7#, or 1...gxf6 allows 2.Qxh7#, or 1...h6 2.Qh7#.

548) **1.Qd8+! Kxd8 2.Ba5+ Ke8 3.Rd8#.**

549) 1.Qh5+! Nxh5 2.fxe6+ Kg6 3.Bc2+ Kg5 4.Rf5+ Kg6 [4..Kg4 5.h3+ Kg3 6.Re3+ Kh4 7.Re4+ Nf4 8.Rexf4+ Kg3 9.Rg4#, or if instead 5...Kh4, then 6.Re4+ and now 6...Nf4 transposes to the above line while 6...Kg3 allows 7.Rg4#] **5.Rf6+ Kg5 6.Rg6+ Kh4** [6...Kf4 7.Re4+ Kf5 8.Rh4#] **7.Re4+ Nf4 8.Rxf4+ Kh5 9.g3!** and 10 Rh4# cannot be stopped.

550) 1.Qxf7+! Kxf7 2.Bxd5+ Kg6 [2...Ke7 3.Rf7#] **3.Bf7+ Kxg5 4.Bc1+ Kg4 5.Rf4+ Kg5 6.h4+ Kh6 7.Rf6+** and mate.

551) 1...Rxg2 2.dxe7 Rxe1+ 3.Bxe1 Rd2+! [Not 3...Rg5+ since White has 4.Rd5!] **4.Kg1 Bd4+ 5.Bf2** [If 5.Kf1, then 5...Bg2#] **5..Rxd1+ 6.Qe1 Rxe1#.**

552) 1...e2+ 2.Rf2 Qxa1+.

553) 1...Qxd4! 2.Bxd4 e3+ 3.Qg2 [after 3.Qf3 Bxf3+ 4.Rxf3 Nxc2 5.Rd1 Nxd4 6.Rxd4 Bc5 Black has a winning pawn up ending] **3...Bxg2+ 4.Kxg2 Nxc2 5.Ra4** [on 5.Rad1 Black has 5...Rxc3! 6.Bxc3 e2] **5...Rfd8 6.Bb6 Rd2+ 7.Kf3 Rxc3! 8.bxc3 e2** winning a piece.

554) 1...Qxg3 2.fxg3 Rd8+ and **3...Rxc8.**

555) 1...Qxg2+ 2.Kxg2 Nf5+ and **3...Nxh6.**

556) 1...Rxg2+! 2.Kxg2 Rxf2+! 3.Bxf2 e3+ 4.Rd5 Qxf2+ 5.Kh1 Qxe1+ 6.Kg2 Qf2+ 7.Kh1 e2 and wins quickly.

557) 1...Ng3+! 2.hxg3 hxg3+ 3.Bxh5 Qh4#.

558) 1.Bf8+! Bh5 2.Qxh5+ gxh5 3.Rh6#.

559) 1.Qxg8+! Ke7 [1...Kxg8 2.Nf6#!] **2.Nd6 Rxd8 3.Qxf7#.**

560) 1.Re7! Kg8 [on 1...Qxe7 2.f6+ wins the Queen) **2.Rxa7** winning easily.

561) 1.Rxh6+ Kxh6 2.Nxd5+ and **3.Nxe7.**

562) 1.Rxd6! Qxd6 2.Bxg7+ Kg8 3.c5+ and wins the Queen.

563) 1.Qxh6 gxh6 2.gxh6+ Kf8 3.Rg8+! Kxg8 4.h7+ Kf8 5.h8=Q#.

564) 1.Ne6+ exf4 2.Bg7#.

565) 1.b4 Nc4 [or 1...Nc6 2.Bd5+ and 3.Rxc6] 2.Bxc4+.

566) 1.Nxg7! Kxg7 2.Qxh6+! Kxh6 3.Bxf6#.

567) 1...Nxh2 2.Qxh2 Qxh2+ 3.Kxh2 f3+ 4.Nxd6 fxe2 winning.

568) 1.Qxg6+! Kxg6 2.Bh5+ Kxh7 3.Bf7#.

569) 1.Qxa7+ Kxa7 2.Ra3+ Kb7 3.Ba6+ Ka8 4.Bc8#.

570) 1.Rg7+ Kf8 2.Rxd7+ Kg8 3.Rg7+ Kf8 4.Rb7+ Kg8 5.Rxb8+ Nf8 6.Rxf8#.

571) 1.Qxh7+ Qxh7 2.Rxh7+ Kxh7 3.Rh1+ Bh2 4.Rxh2+ Kg7 5.Bh6+ Kh7 6.Bxf8#.

572) 1.Ng6+! fxg6 2.fxg6+ and wins the exchange next move.

573) 1.Qxh5+ Bxh5 2.f7+ e5 3.Bxe5#.

574) 1...Nd4+ 2.Nd2 Rxd2+ 3.Rxd2 Nf3+ and 4...Nxd2.

575) 1.Qa8+ Nb8 2.Qxb7+! Kxb7 3.Bxd7+ Ka8 4.Rxb8+! Kxb8 5.Rb1+ Ka8 6.Bc6#.

576) **1...Qxf6! 2.Qc1** [after 2.Qxf6 Re1+ 3.Bf1 Rxf1+! 4.Rxf1 f2#] **2...Qb2!** [the same theme: 3.Rxb2 f2+ 4.Be4 Bxe4# or 3.Qxb2 Re1+ as above] **3.Qf1 Qxf2 4.Qxf2 Re1+ 5.Qxe1 f2 + 6.Qe4 Bxe4+ 7.Bxe4 f1=Q#.**

577) **1.Rg3+! fxg3 2.Bxh7+ Kxh7 3.hxg3+ Kg8 4.Rh8#.**

578) **1.Nh5 gxh5 2.Bxh7+ Kh8 3.Bg6+ Kg8 4.Qh7+ Kf8 5.Bh6+ Ke7 6.Qxf7+ Kd8 7.Qxe8#.**

579) **1.Qh5+!! Kg7** [on 1...Kxh5 2.Nf7+ Bg5 3.Rxg5#] **2.Qh7+ Kf8 3.Qxa7 Ne7 4.Rxf6+ Qxf6 5.Nh7+** wins.

580) **1.Nc5+** wins the Black Queen.

581) **1.Rh8+ Kxh8 2.e6+ Qg7 3.Bxg7+**

582) **1.Qxf7+! Kxf7 2.dxc6+ Kg6 3.cxb7** and after 4.bxa8=Q White will be a Rook up.

583) **1...Bxd4! 2.Rxh5 e2+ 3.Kh1 e1=Q#.**

584) **1.Nxg5+ Bxg5 2.Rxg5 Bxc4 3.Rxg7+ Kh8 4.Rxd7+ Kg8 5.Rg7+ Kh8 6.Rc7+ Kg8 7.Rxc4** with an easily won ending.

585) **1.Bxe7 Nxa4 2.Bxd6+ Kd7 3.Bxf8 Rhxf8 4.Ne5+** and 5.Nxg4.

586) **1.Bh5+ g6 2.Nxg6 Nb6** [2...hxg6 3.Bxg6#] **3.Ne5#.**

587) **1.d5+!**

588) **1.Qc5+ Re7 2.Ng6+! Kxf7** [or 2...hxg6 3.Rh8+ Kxf7 4.fxg5+ Ke6 5.Re1+ Kd7 6.Rxe7#, or 5...Kf7 6.Rxe7#] **3.fxg5+ Kg8** [3..Kxg6 4.Qf5#] **4.Nxe7+ Kh8 5.Ng6+ Kg8 6.Qf8+! Rxf8 7.Rxf8#.**

589) 1.Qd5 Qc1+ 2.Rf1+.

590) 1.Rh1 Kh5 2.Kg3+ and wins the Bishop.

591) 1.Rd7+ Rc7 2.Rxc7+ Kxc7 3.Bf8+ and 4.Bxg7.

592) 1...Nh4+ 2.Ke1 [or 2.Kg1 Qg4#] 2...Nxf3#.

593) 1. Nf6+! Kxf6 2.Nh5+ Kf7 3.Qh7#.

594) 1...Bxf5! winning a piece. If 2.Bxf5 Rxg3+! 3. fxg3 [3.K moves 3...Qxh4+ mates] 3...d3+ wins the Queen.

595) 1.Qg8+!! and wins. 1...Kxg8 2.Be6+ Kh8 3.Rg8#.

596) 1...Bh3!! 2.Qxa8 Bc5+ 3.Kh1 [3.Red4 Bxd4+ 4.Rxd4 Qe1#] **3...Bxg2+!** **4.Kxg2 Qg4+ 5.Kf1** [5.Kh1 Qf3#] **5...Qf3+ 6.Ke1 Qf2#.**

597) **1.Nxf7! Rxd8** [1...Nxd3 2.Ng5+ Kh6 3.Rxh7#] **2.Nxd8+ Kf6 3.Nxe6** with a winning position.

598) 1.Rxd7! Qxd7 2.Nxe5 Qc8 3.Bxb7 Qxb7 4.Ng6! Bf6 5.Ne7+! Kh8 6.Qxf6! gxf6 7.Bxf6#.

599) 1.Bh7+ Kh8 2.Bg8+! Kxg8 [2...Bh6 3.Qh7#] **3.Qh7#.**

600) 1.Qxd8+! Kxd8 2.Bc2+ and 3.Bxa4.

601) 1...Ng3! 2.Qxg6 Nde2#.

602) 1...Rxf1+! 2.Kxf1 Bd3+ and 3...Qxf4.

603) 1...Nf3+! 2.gxf3 [2.Kh1 Nxd4] 2...Qg6+ 3.Kh1 Ng3+ 4.hxg3 Qxc2.

604) 1.Rxf6! gxf6 2.Qxd7+! Kxd7 3.dxc5+ followed by cxb6.

605) 1...d3! 2.Bxf6 [2.Qxd3 Qxb2] 2...dxe2.

606) 1...Qc1+ 2.Kh2 Qf4+ 3.Kh1 [3.Kg1 Nf3+ and 4...Qxd6] 3...Qf1+ 4.Kh2 Qxe2.

607) 1...Nxf2! 2.Kxf2 Bxg3+ and 3...Qxd1.

608) 1.Nf7! Qf6 [1...Kxf7 2.fxg5+ winning the Queen] 2.fxg5 winning material.

609) 1...Bxd3! 2.Qxd3 Bxh2+ 3.Nxh2 Rxd3.

610) 1...Ne3! 2.Re1 Nc4+ 3.Bxc4 Rxe1.

611) 1...Qxd2! 2.Rxd2 Rxc2 3.Rxc2 Rxc2 4.Qa3 [4.Qa1 amounts to the same thing] 4...Rxg2+ 5.Kh1 Rxa2+ and 6...Rxa3.

612) 1.Nd6 Re7 [or 1...Rg8 2.Nf7#] 2.Nxc8 Rxc8 3.Bxe7.

613) 1...Nxd4 2.Qxd4 Ng4+ and 3...Bxd4.

614) 1...Nxe4 2.Qxe5 Nxd2+ 3.Kc1 Bxe5 4.Kxd2 Rxb4.

615) 1...Nc7! attacking both the Bb5 and Ne5.

616) 1.Nxe6! Qxd3 [1...fxe6 2.Bxc5] **2.Nxg7+! Kf8 3.Bxc5+! Kxg7 4.exd3** winning material.

617) 1.Ng5! and wins. If 1...Nxg5 2.Qg7#.

618) 1...Nd3 2.Rd1 Qh1+ 3.Ke2 Nf4+! 4.Kf3 [or 4.exf4 Qxd1+ 5.Ke3 Qd3#] **4...Qxg2+** wins the Queen.

619) 1...Bxc5 2.Qxh8 Ne5 [threatening to play 3...Qg4!] **3.Kh1 Bxg2+ 4.Kxg2 Qg4+ 5.Kh1 Qe4+ 6.Kg1 Nf3+ 7.Kg2 Nh4+ 8.Kg3 Qg2+ 9.Kxh4 Be7+ 10.Bg5 Bxg5#.**

620) 1.Rxe5! Qxe5 2.Ng6! and now on **2...Qxh2 3.Nde7#!**

621) 1...Nxc5 2.dxc5 [2.Bxc8 Nd3+ retains the extra pawn and a much better position) **2...Bxf5.**

622) 1.Qxb5!! Qxb5 2.c4 Qd7 3.Rxg7+ Kh8 4.Rg8+ Kxg8 5.Rg1+ Qg4 6.Rxg4#.

623) 1.Nb6 Ra7 2.Nxe5 Qxe5 3.Nxc8 Rxc8 4.Bxf7+ and **5.Rxc8.**

624) 1.f7+ Kh7 [1...Bg7 2.f8=Q+] **2.Qf5+ Kh8 3.Qf6+ Kh7 4.g6+** and **5.Qxh4.**

625) 1...Rxe2 2.Qxe2 Qc3+ 3.Qc2 Qxc2#.

626) 1.Nb5! cxb5 2.Qxc7+ Bxc7 3.Rxc7 Kxc7 4.Nxe6+ Kd7 5.Nxd8 Rxd8 6.Bxb5 with a winning position.

627) 1.Rxg7+! Bxg7 2.Qg4 Qxf5 [2...Rg6 3.Nh6+ picks up the Queen] **3.Qxf5 Rf6 4.Qd7!** and wins.

628) 1...Be3!! and wins, since white cannot defend the Bf2 and the threat of Qxg2# simultaneously.

8. DIVERSION

Diversion is a motif in which we divert an enemy piece from an important post. Once the piece is diverted we can then exploit the new setting to attack other vital elements of the opponent's position. Often the diverted piece is charged with protecting another. Its diversion leaves the other piece underdefended and hence vulnerable. This type of operation is also called removing the guard and occurs with great frequency in chess. Close examination of these examples will pay great dividends.

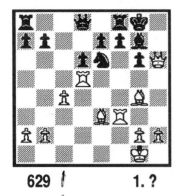 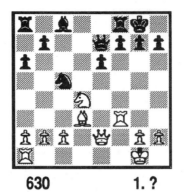 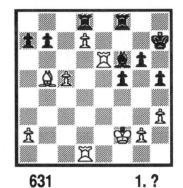

629 **!**   1. ?   630   1. ?   631   1. ?

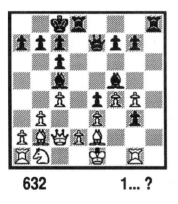 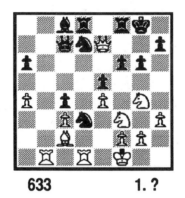 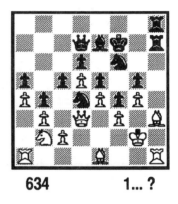

632   1... ?   633   1. ?   634   1... ?

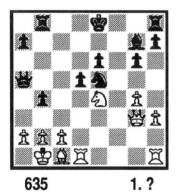 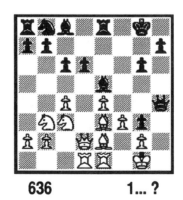 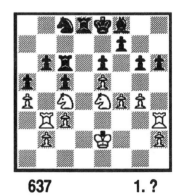

635   1. ?   636   1... ?   637   1. ?

DIVERSION

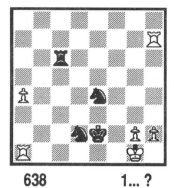

638   1... ?

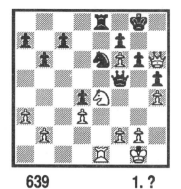

639   1. ?

640   1... ?

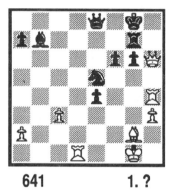

641   1. ?

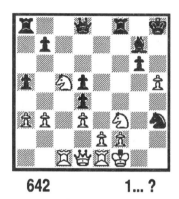

642   1... ?

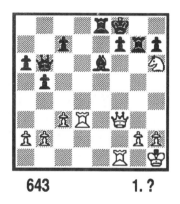

643   1. ?

644   1... ?

645   1. ?

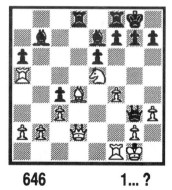

646   1... ?

DIVERSION

129

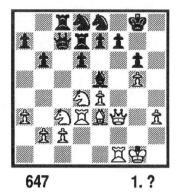

647   1. ?

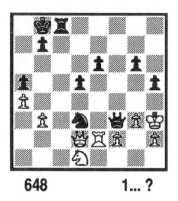

648   1... ?

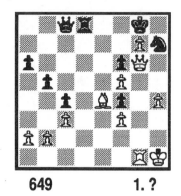

649   1. ?

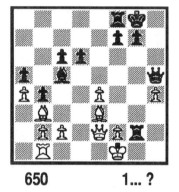

650   1... ?

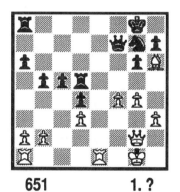

651   1. ?

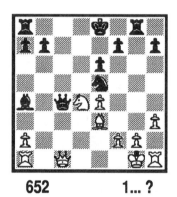

652   1... ?

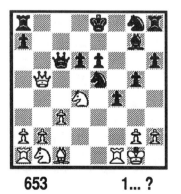

653   1... ?

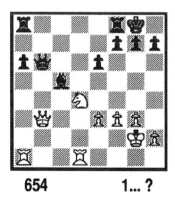

654   1... ?

655   1. ?

DIVERSION

130

656   1... ?

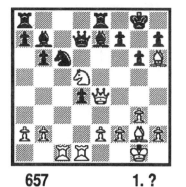

657   1. ?

658   1... ?

659   1... ?

660   1... ?

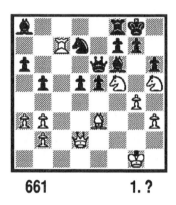

661   1. ?

662   1... ?

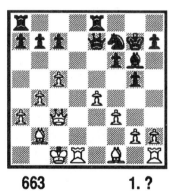

663   1. ?

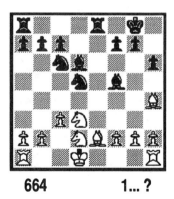

664   1... ?

DIVERSION

665   1... ?

666   1... ?

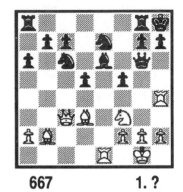

667   1. ?

668   1... ?

669   1. ?

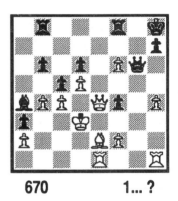

670   1... ?

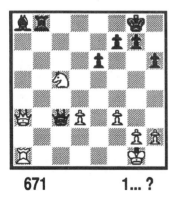

671   1... ?

672   1... ?

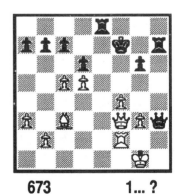

673   1... ?

DIVERSION

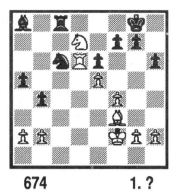

674   1. ?

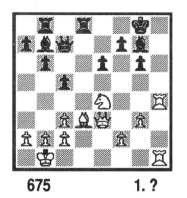

675   1. ?

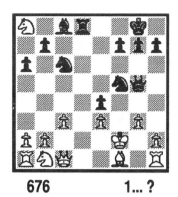

676   1... ?

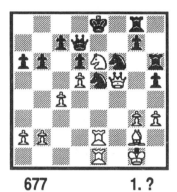

677   1. ?

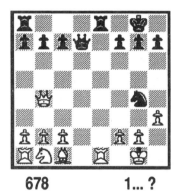

678   1... ?

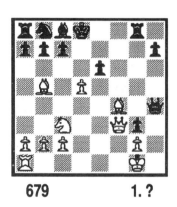

679   1. ?

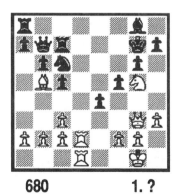

680   1. ?

681   1... ?

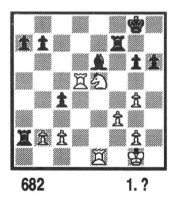

682   1. ?

DIVERSION

133

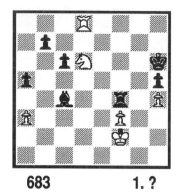

683　　　　　1. ?

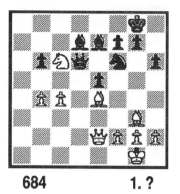

684　　　　　1. ?

685　　　　　1... ?

686　　　　　1... ?

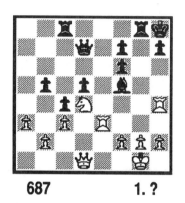

687　　　　　1. ?

688　　　　　1... ?

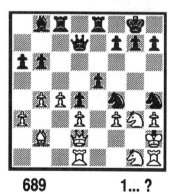

689　　　　　1... ?

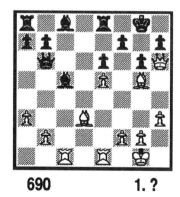

690　　　　　1. ?

691　　　　　1... ?

DIVERSION

134

692   1. ?

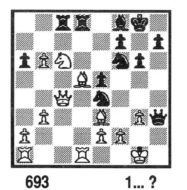

693   1... ?

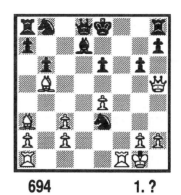

694   1. ?

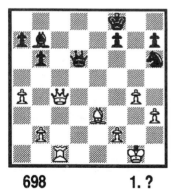

695   1. ?

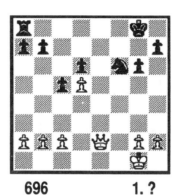

696   1. ?

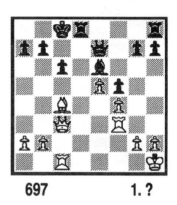

697   1. ?

698   1. ?

699   1. ?

700   1... ?

DIVERSION

701　　　　　1. ?

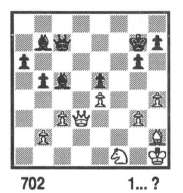

702　　　　　1... ?

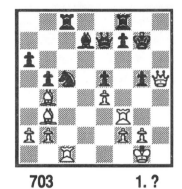

703　　　　　1. ?

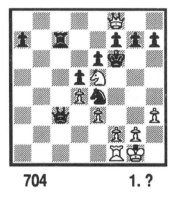

704　　　　　1. ?

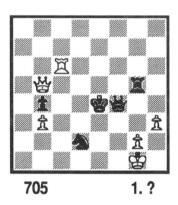

705　　　　　1. ?

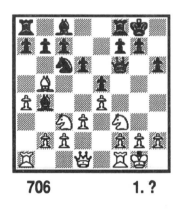

706　　　　　1. ?

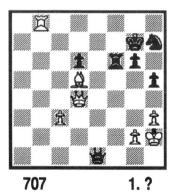

707　　　　　1. ?

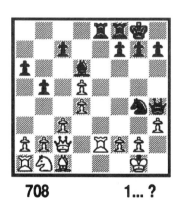

708　　　　　1... ?

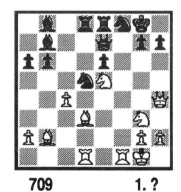

709　　　　　1. ?

DIVERSION

136

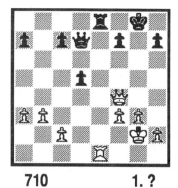

710   1. ?

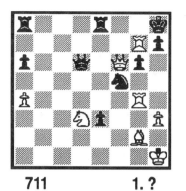

711   1. ?

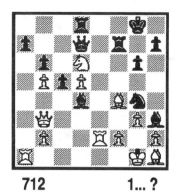

712   1... ?

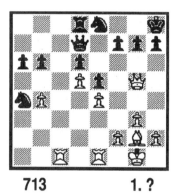

713   1. ?

714   1. ?

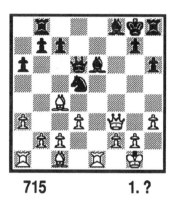

715   1. ?

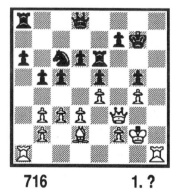

716   1. ?

717   1. ?

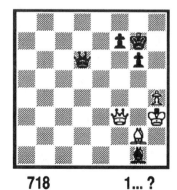

718   1... ?

DIVERSION

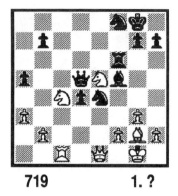

719   1. ?

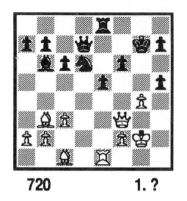

720   1. ?

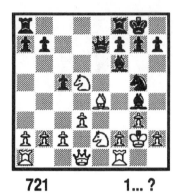

721   1... ?

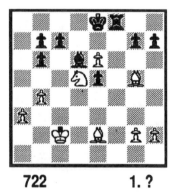

722   1. ?

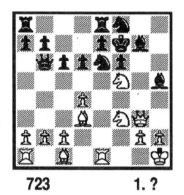

723   1. ?

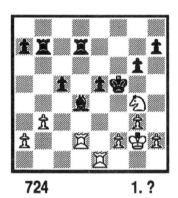

724   1. ?

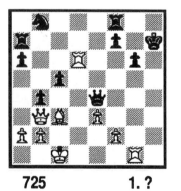

725   1. ?

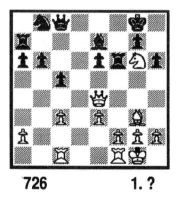

726   1. ?

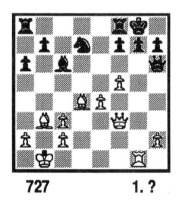

727   1. ?

DIVERSION

138

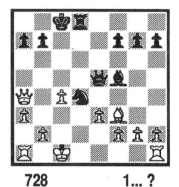

728   1... ?

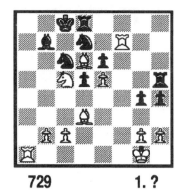

729   1. ?

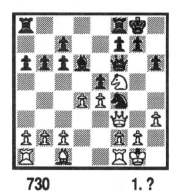

730   1. ?

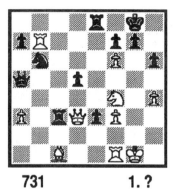

731   1. ?

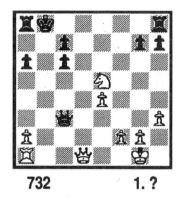

732   1. ?

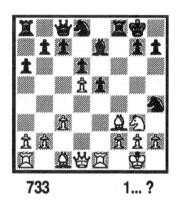

733   1... ?

734   1. ?

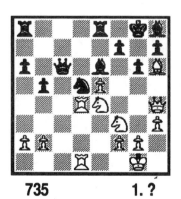

735   1. ?

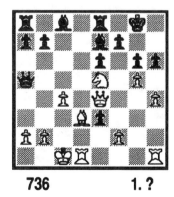

736   1. ?

DIVERSION

139

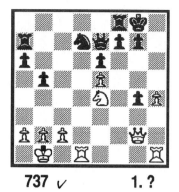

737 ✓   1. ?

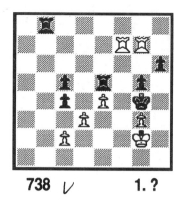

738 ✓   1. ?

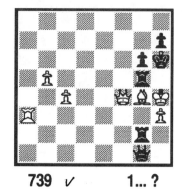

739 ✓   1... ?

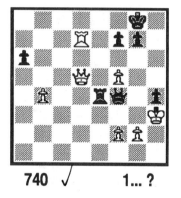

740 ✓   1... ?

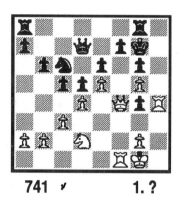

741 ✓   1. ?

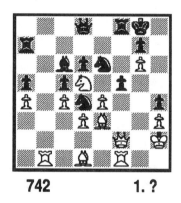

742   1. ?

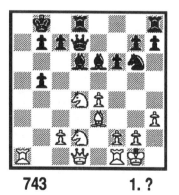

743   1. ?

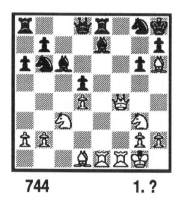

744   1. ?

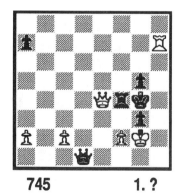

745   1. ?

DIVERSION

140

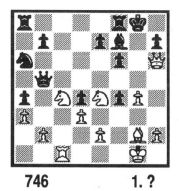

746   1. ?

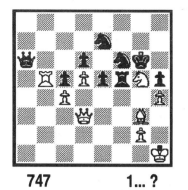

747   1... ?

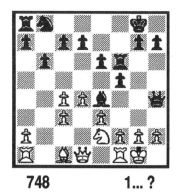

748   1... ?

749   1... ?

DIVERSION

629) 1.Qxg6!! Nf4 [1...Nc7 2.Qxg7+! and the Rooks mate] **2.Rxf4 fxg6 3.Bxe6+ Rf7** [3...Kh7 4.Rh4+ Bh6 5.Bxh6 Rf5 (5...g5 6.Rxg5 Qb6 7.c5 and wins) 6.Rxf5 gxf5 7.Bf7 e5 8.Rh3! and it is over for Black] **4.Rxf7 Kh8** [4...Be5 5.Rf5 winning] **5.Rg5! b5 6.Rg3** and White wins.

630) 1.Bxh7+ Kxh7 2.Rh3+ Kg8 3.Nf5! [3.Qh5? f6 and Black is O.K.] **3...Qg5 4.Qh5!!** [now 4...Qxh5 5. Ne7+! Kh7 6. Rh5#, or 4...f6 5.Ne7#].

631) 1.Ba6!! bxa6 [if 1...Rb8 2.Bxb7 Rxb7 3.Rxf6 Rd8 4.c6! with a crush] **2.c6 Kg7 3.c7 Kf7 4.Rc6 Rc8 5.Rxf6!** and wins [5...Kxf6 6.d8=Q+].

632) 1...Rh1!! 2.Rxh1 [2.Kf1 Rxg1+ 3.Kxg1 Qh4 winning] **2...g2 3.Rf1** [if 3.Rg1 Qh4+ 4.Kd1 Qh1 5.Qc3 Qxg1+ 6.Kc2 Qf2 7.gxf5 Qxe2 8.Na3 Bb4!] **3...Qh4+ 4.Kd1 gxf1=Q+** [5.Bxf1 Bxg4+ and Black wins]. A Spassky original!

633) 1.Rxd3! cxd3 2.Bb3+ Kh8 3.Nf6!! Rxf6 4.Ng5 Rxf2+ 5.Kg1 [5.Kxf2? Qc5+ and Black wins!] **5...Rf1+ 6.Kh2** winning.

634) 1...Nxg4! 2.fxg4 [2.Bxg4 Rxh1] **2...Rxh3! 3.Rxh3 Qxg4+ 4.Kh2 Rxh3+ 5.Qxh3 Nf3+ 6.Qxf3 Qxf3** and wins.

635) 1.Bh6! Qc7 [1...Bxh6 2.Qxe5 Kd7 3.Qd6+ Kc8 4.Qxe6+ with a win] **2.Nd6+! Kd8** [2...Qxd6 Bxg7 or 2...Kf8 3.Rhf1+ Kg8 4.Rf7 Qxf7 5.Nxf7 Kxf7 6.Bxg7 Qxg7 7.Qe5+] **3.Bxg7 Kxg7 4.Qxe5!** winning, as 4...Qxe5 is met by 5.Nf7+.

636) 1...Bf4! [if 1...Qh2+ 2.Kf1 Qh1+ 3.Bg1] **2.Qd3 Qh2+ 3.Kf1 Bh3! 4.gxh3 g2+** and wins.

637) 1.Nxa5! bxa5 2.Nf6+ Ke7 3.Rb7+ winning.

638) 1...Nf3+! and wins. 2.gxf3 is met by 2...Rg6+ 3.Kh1 Nf2#. If 2.Kh1 Nf2# immediately.

639) 1.Nd6! winning. On 1...cxd6 2.Rxe6! [with threats on g7].

640) 1...Ng3+! and wins. On 2.Qxg3 Rxb1 and on 2.hxg3 comes Ra8!! with the devastating Rh8 to follow.

641) 1.Rd8! Qxd8 2.Qh8+ Kf7 3.Qxd8 g5 4.Rh6 winning.

642) 1...Qh4!! and wins. on 2.Nxh4 Rxf2 is mate, and on 2.Kg2 comes 2...Nf4+ 3.Kg1 Qg4+.

643) 1.Rd7! Rb8 [on 1...Bxd7 2.Qxf7+ Rxf7 3.Rxf7#] **2.Nxf7 Bxd7 3.Nd8+.**

644) 1...Rxf3! 2.Qxf3 [2.Rg1 Raf8] **2...Bg4! 3.Qf2 Bf3+ 4.Kg1 Bxh2+!** and wins. If 5.Qxh2 Rg8+, or Kf1 Qh3+.

645) 1.Bb6!! Qxb6 [1...axb6 2.Qd8#] **2.Qh4+ Rf6** [2...f6 3.Qh7+] **3.Qxb4+** and wins.

646) 1...Rxd4! 2.cxd4 Bb4! 3.Ra3 [g2 must remain protected] **3...Qxa3!** and wins, since on 3.bxa3 comes 3...Bxd2.

647) 1.Ne6! Nxe6 [on 1...fxe6 White mates with 2.Qf8+ Kh7 3.Qh6+ Kg8 4.Rf8#] **2.Qxf7+ Kh8 3.Qxe6** winning easily.

648) 1...Rc2! and wins [2.Qxc2 Nf4+ 3.Kh4 Qg4#].

649) 1.Qe8+! wins [1...Rxe8 2.Bd5+].

650) 1...Rg1+ 2.Kxg1 Qxe2.

651) 1.Re7! Qxe7 2.Qxd5+ picking up the Ra8.

652) 1...Qxd4! 2.Bxd4 Nf3+ 3.Kf1 Bb5+ 4.Qc4 Bxc4#.

653) 1...Nf3+! 2.Kh1 [on 2.gxf3 Bxd4+ and 3...Qxb5, same for 2.Rxf3] **2...Nxd4 3.Qxc6+ Nxc6** winning a piece.

654) 1...Bxd4 2.Qxb6 Bxb6.

655) 1.Bxc5! Qxf3 2.Re1+ Be7 3.Rxe7+ Kf8 4.Rd8#.

656) 1...Rxg2+ 2.Kxg2 Qxe4+.

657) 1.Qxe7 Rxe7 [or 1...Qxe7 2.Nxe7+ Rxe7 3.Bxc6 winning a piece] **2.Nf6+ Kh8 3.Nxd7 Rxd7 4.Bxc6.**

658) 1...Nc2+ 2.Qxc2 Qxe2#.

659) 1...Nxe2! 2.Rxb4 [If 2.Kxe2 Qxc3 while 2.Nxe2 allows 2..Qxb1+] **2...Bxc3** and Black emerges a piece ahead.

660) 1...Qc4! 2.Qxc4 [or 2.Nc3 Qxe2 and 3...Rxd1+] **2...Rxd1+ 3.Qf1 Bd4+ 4.Kh1 Rxf1#.**

661) 1.Rxd7! Qxd7 2.Nf6+ gxf6 3.Bc5! Rc8 4.Qxh6 and mate at g7.

662) 1...Nc4 2.Rc2 Nxb2 3.Rxb2 Rxc3.

663) 1.Rd7! Qxd7 2.Qxf6+ Kh6 3.Qg7+ Kh5 4.g4+ Kh4 5.Bd4 and 6.Bf2 will mate.

664) 1...Rxe2! 2.Kxe2 Re8+ 3.Kd1 [or 3.Kf1] **3...Bxd3** wins two pieces for the Rook.

665) 1...Be2! and Black wins the exchange leaving himself two pawns up.

666) 1...Rxd3+ 2.Kxd3 Rxf2.

144

667) 1.Rxe6! Qxe6 2.Ng5 Qg6 3.Rxh7+ Qxh7 4.Nf7#.

668) 1...Rh1+ 2.Kxh1 Qxf2.

669) 1.Qc2+ Qg6 [1...g6 2.Rd7+ Kg8 3.Qc4+! Kh8 4.Qc8+ mates] **2.Rh8+ Kxh8 3.Qxg6.**

670) 1...Bc2+ 2.Kxc2 Qxe4+.

671) 1...Rb1+! 2.Rxb1 [if 2.Kf2 then 2...Qe1 is mate] **2...Qxa3.**

672) 1...Rxb2+ 2.Qxb2 Bd3+ 3.Kc3 [or 3.Kc1 Ba3] **3...Bb4+! 4.Qxb4 Qc2#.**

673) 1...Re3! 2.Qg2 [2.Qxe3 Qh1#] **2...Rxg3.**

674) 1.Nb6 Rb8 2.Nxa8 Rxa8 3.Bxc6.

675) 1.Rh8+! Bxh8 2.Rxh8+ Kxh8 3.Qh6+ Kg8 4.Nf6#.

676) 1...Rd1! 2.Qxd1 Qxe3+ 3.Kg2 Nh4+! 4.gxh4 Bh3#.

677) 1.Rxe5! dxe5 2.Rxe5 [threatening 3.Nc5+] **2...Kf7 3.Ng5+ Kf8 4.Re6!** [threat: 5.Rxf6+ and 6.Qxd7] **4...Qa4 5.b3 Qxa2 6.Re8+! Kxe8 7.Qe6+ Kd8** [7...Kf8 8.Qf7#] **8.Nf7#.**

678) 1...Qd6! 2.Qc3 [if 2.Qxd6 then 2...Rxe1#] **2...Qh2+ 3.Kf1 Qh1#.**

679) 1.Bxg3 Qg5 [1...Qxg3 2.Qf6#, or 1...Rxg3 2.Qf8#] **2.Qf7! e5 3.Qxg8+! Qxg8 4.Bh4+ Qg5 5.Bxg5#.**

680) 1.Qxc7+ Qxc7 2.Rd7+ Qxd7 3.Rxd7+ and 4.Bxc6 winning a piece.

681) 1...Bh4! 2.Qxh4 Qxc2+ and 3...Qxb2.

682) 1.Rd6 Rf6 [1...Re7 2.Nxg6] **2.Nd7** winning the exchange after 2...Bxd7 3.Rxf6.

683) 1.Kg3 Rd4 2.Nf5+.

684) 1.Bxe5 Qe6 2.Bd5 Qg4 [on 2...Nxd5 3.cxd5 Qg6 (or 3...Qxd5 or 3...Qf5) 4.Nxe7+ wins the Queen] **3.Qxg4 Nxg4 4.Nxe7+.**

685) 1...Bxc3 2.bxc3 g5 3.Nd3 Rxe2.

686) 1...Bxd6 2.Qxd6 [2.Bxd6 loses to 2...Rxf2+] **2...Rxf2+ 3.Bxf2 Qxf2+ 4.Kh1 Be4+ 5.Rf3 Bxf3#.**

687) 1.Re7! Qe7 2.Nxf5 Qf8 3.Rxh7+! Kxh7 4.Qh5+ Qh6 5.Qxh6#.

688) 1...Rd2! winning. [2.Qe3 Nc4 3.Qf4 Qxc5].

689) 1...Qxh3+! 2.Nxh3 Nxf3#.

690) 1.Rxc5! Qxc5 2.Bb5! Qf8 [after 2...Qxb5 3.Bf6 mates next] **3.Bxe8 Qxe8 4.Bf6 Qf8 5.Qxf8+ Kxf8 6.Rd1 Bd7 7.Rxd7** winning handily.

691) 1...Nd4! 2.Nxd4 [on Queen moves, 2...Nxf3+ followed by 3...Qh2#] **2...Qh2#.**

692) 1.Bxf7+! Qxf7 2.Rd8+ Kxd8 3.Qxf7.

693) 1...Rxd5! 2.Rxd5 Rxc6! 3.Bc5 [3.Qxc6 Ng4!] **3...Rxc5 4.Rxc5 Bxc5** winning.

694) 1.Qxh7 Rxh7 2.Rf8#.

695) 1.Re1! Rxe1 [1...Kd7 2.Rxe6 Kxe6 3.Qxc6+] **2.Qxc6+ Ke7 3.Qxa8.**

146

696) **1.Qe6+ Kg7 2.Qe7+** wins the Knight.

697) 1.Qa3! Qf7 [1...Qxa3 2.Bxe6+ and 3.bxa3] **2.Bxe6+ Qxe6 3.Qxa7** winning an important pawn.

698) 1.Qc7! Qxc7 [1...Qd5 2.Bxh6+] **2.Bxh6+ Ke8 3.Rxc7.**

699) 1.Nxg6! fxg6 2.Rxg6+ Kf7 [2...Kh8 3.Rxf6 Qxf6 4.Qxh5] **3.Rxf6+ Kxf6 4.Qxh5** with a winning position.

700) 1...d3+ 2.Kh1 Qf2! 3.Qxd3 Bxe4 4.fxe4 Qxf1+ 5.Qxf1 Ra8! and wins.

701) 1.Bf5 Rxe1+ 2.Qxe1 Qd6 3.Qe8+ Qf8 4.Bxh7+ winning Black's Queen.

702) 1...Qd8! 2.Qf3 [2.Qxd8 Be4#] **2...Qd1! 3.Kg2 Qc2+ 4.Kh3 Bxe4** and wins.

703) 1.Rxc5 Rxc5 2.Bxc5 Qxc5 3.Qxg5+ Kh7 4.Qh5+ Kg7 5.Rg3+ Kf6 6.Qg5#.

704) 1.Qd8+ Re7 [not 1...Kf5 2.g4#] **2.Nd7+** wins the Rook next move.

705) 1.Qxb4+ Kf5 [1...Ke3 2.Rc3+] **2.Rf6+ Kxf6 3.Qxf4+.**

706) 1.Nd5 Qd8 2.Bxc6 bxc6 3.Nxb4.

707) 1.Rb7+ Kh6 2.Rxh7+ Kxh7 3.Qxf6.

708) 1...Qxf2+! 2.Rxf2 Re1+ 3.Rf1 Bh2+! 4.Kh1 Rxf1#.

709) 1.Rxf8+! Kxf8 [If 1...Qxf8 then 2.Qxh7#] **2.Ng6+ hxg6 3.Qh8+ Kf7 4.Qxg7#.**

710) 1.Qg4+! Qxg4 2.Rxe8+ Kg7 3.fxg4.

711) 1.Rh4! Nxh4 [1...Qxf6 2.Rhxh7# or 1...Nxg7 2.Qxd6] 2.Qxd6.

712) 1...Qxd6!! 2.Bxd6 Rxf2 3.Re3 Rxb2 4.Bg2 Bxe3+ 5.Qxe3 Rxg2+ followed by Nxe3.

713) 1.Bh3! f6 [on 1...Qxh3 2.Qxd8] 2.Bxd7 fxg5 3.Bxa4.

714) 1.Qxc6+! Bxc6 2.Nxe6#.

715) 1.Rxe6 Qxe6 2.Bxd5.

716) 1.Rh7+ Kxh7 2.Qxf7+ Kh8 [or h6] 3.Rh1#.

717) 1.Rxg7 Rh8 [1...Rxg7 2.Qxh5+ Kd8 3.Qh8+ and mate next] 2.Qxh5+! Rxh5 3.Rg8#.

718) 1...Qh2+! 2.Kg4 f5+ 3.Kg5 Qxg2+!! 4.Qxg2 Be3#.

719) 1.g4! Bg6 2.Nxg6 Nxg6 3.Qxe4.

720) 1.Bh6+! Kxh6 [1...Kh8 2.Qxf6+ Qg7 3.Bxg7#, or 1...Kg6 2.gxh5+ Kxh6 3.Qxf6+ Kxh5 4.Rh1+ mates] 2.Qxf6#.

721) 1...Qxe4+! 2.dxe4 Bf3+ 3.Kg1 Nh3#.

722) 1.Nxc7+ Bxc7 2.Bb5#!

723) 1.Qxg7+!! Nxg7 2.Nh6#!

724) 1.Rxd4! and mate in two follows on any recapture of the Rook.

148

725) 1.Qc4!! and wins. [1...Qxc4 Rh1mates. If 1...Re7 there follows 2.Qxe4 followed by 3.Rh1+. Finally if the Queen retreats along the h1-a8 diagonal, 2.Qh4+ is allowed].

726) 1.Qa8!! and wins. [Capturing the Queen results in 2. Nxe7+ followed by 3.Nxc8, and on 1...Rb7 2.Nxe7+ Rxe7 3.Qxb8].

727) 1.Qh3! and wins. [1...Qxh3 2.Rxg7+ Kh8 3.Rxf7+ Kg8 4.Rg7+ Kh8 5.Rg8+ and mate.

728) 1...Qa5! and wins. [on 2.Qxa5 Nb3#, or 2.Qd1 Nb3+ 3.Qxb3 Qd2#].

729) 1.Ra8+! and wins. [1...Bxa8 2.Ba6+, or 1...N6b8 2.Rxb8+ Nxb8 3.Rc7#].

730) 1.dxe5 Qxe5 2.Nxd6 Qxd6 3.Bxf4.

731) 1.Qg6!! and wins. [1...fxg6 2.Rxg7+ followed by 3.Nxg6#].

732) 1.Rb1+ Ka7 [1...Kc8 2.Qd7#] **2.Qd4+! Qxd4 3.Nxc6#.**

733) 1...Rxf3! 2.gxf3 Qh3 and mates.

734) 1.Re8! and Black Resigns.

735) 1.Rxd5! Bxd5 2.Rxd5 Qxd5 3.Nf6+ Bxf6 4.Qxf6 and White wins.

736) 1.Nxf7! and wins. [1...Kxf7 2.Qxg6+ Kf8 3.Qxh6+ Kg8 4.Qh7+ Kf8 5.Bg6 and mate at f7].

737) 1.Rxd7! Rxd7 2.Nf6+! Kh8 [2...gxf6 3.Qxg4+ Kh7 4.Qh5+ followed by 4.Rg1#] **3.Qxg4 g6 4.h5** winning.

738) 1.Rf4+! Kh5 2.Rh4+! gxh4 3.g4#.

739) 1...Qf2+! 2.Qxf2 Rh5+! 3.Bxh5 g5#.

740) 1...Re3+! and wins. [2.fxe3 Qg3#].

741) 1.Rh7+! and wins. [1...Kxh7 2.Qh2+].

742) 1.Rb8!! winning. [1...Qxb8 2.Qxh4!].

743) 1.Ra8+! Kxa8 2.Qa1+ Kb8 3.Qa7+!! Kxa7 4.Nc6+ Ka8 5.Ra1+ with mate to follow.

744) 1.Nh5!! and wins. [1...Nxh6 2.Qxh6 Rg8 3.Rf7].

745) 1.Rh4+!! Kxh4 [1...gxh4 2.Qg6#] 2.Qh7+ Qh5 [2...Kg4 3.Qh3#] 3.fxg3+ Kg4 4.Qd7+ Rf5 5.Qd1+ and wins.

746) 1.Ncd6! and wins. [if 1...exd6 2.Nf6+, or 1...Qxb2 2.Nf5 Qxc1+ 3.Bf1 Qe3+ 4.Kh1!]

747) 1...Qa3!! 2.Qxa3 [2.Rb3 Qxb3!] 2...Rf1+ 3.Kh2 Ng4+ 4.Kh3 Rh1+ 5.Bh2 Nf5! and wins. [6.Qg3 Rxh2+!! 7.Qxh2 Nf2#].

748) 1...Bf3!! winning. [2.gxf3 Rh6 3.Re1 Qxh2+ 4.Kf1 Qh3+ 5.Kg1 Qh1#, or 2.Qd3 Rh6 3.h3 Bxg2, or 2.g3 Qxh2+!].

749) 1...Qf3!! and wins [2.gxf3 Nexf3+ 3.Kh1 Bh3 with mate coming on g2].

9. CLEARANCE

This tactic is used to clear a square or uncover a line (rank, file or diagonal) in order for an effective follow-up to take advantage of the newly cleared square or squares. Very often the piece which clears the way for the follow-up actions of another will sacrifice itself in the process. If this sacrifice involves an attack on the enemy King, then the effect is intensified.

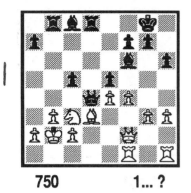

750   1... ?

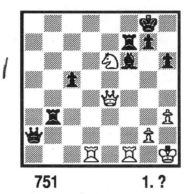

751   1. ?

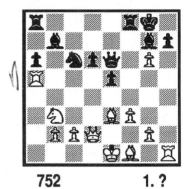

752   1. ?

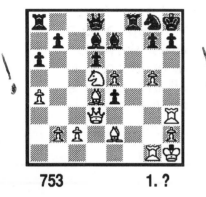

753   1. ?

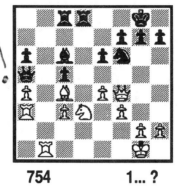

754   1... ?

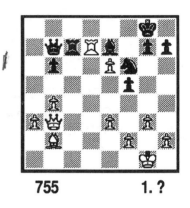

755   1. ?

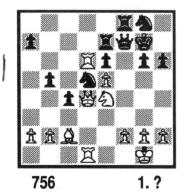

756   1. ?

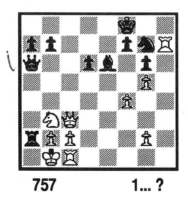

757   1... ?

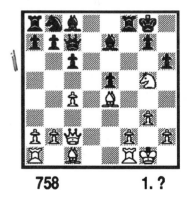

758   1. ?

CLEARANCE

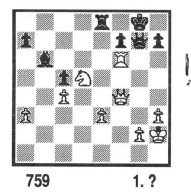

759   1. ?

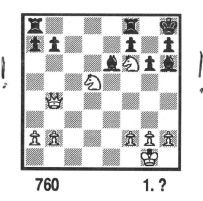

760   1. ?

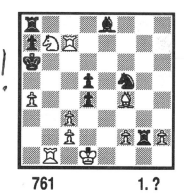

761   1. ?

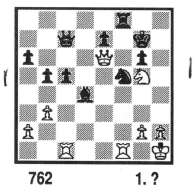

762   1. ?

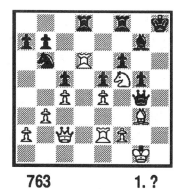

763   1. ?

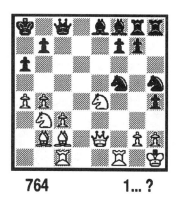

764   1... ?

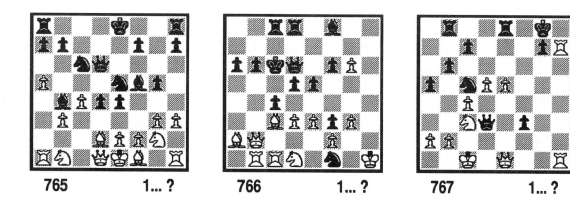

765   1... ?   766   1... ?   767   1... ?

CLEARANCE

153

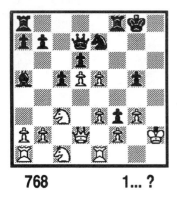

768   1... ?

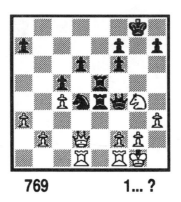

769   1... ?

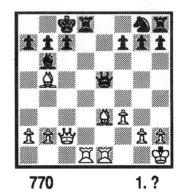

770   1. ?

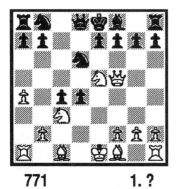

771   1. ?

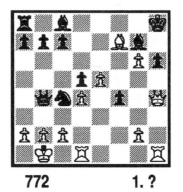

772   1. ?

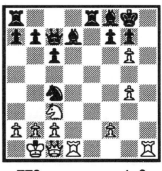

773   1. ?

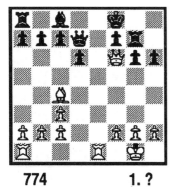

774   1. ?

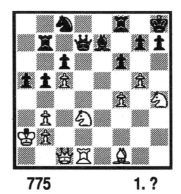

775   1. ?

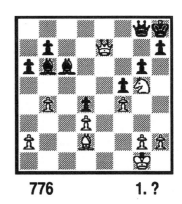

776   1. ?

CLEARANCE

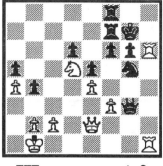

777   1. ?

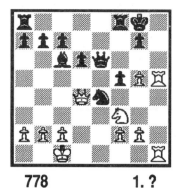

778   1. ?

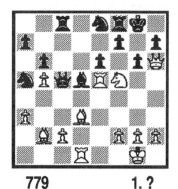

779   1. ?

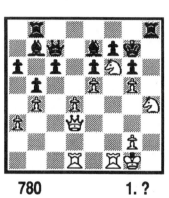

780   1. ?

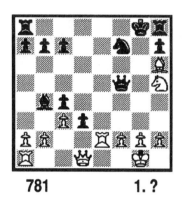

781   1. ?

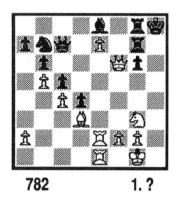

782   1. ?

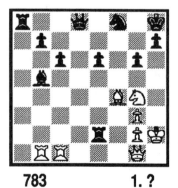

783   1. ?

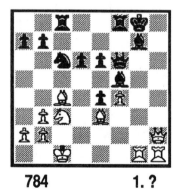

784   1. ?

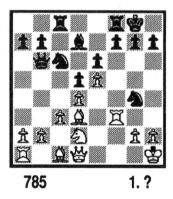

785   1. ?

CLEARANCE

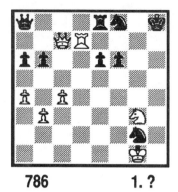 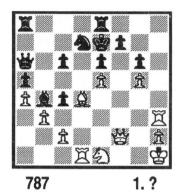 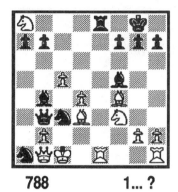

786   1. ?   787   1. ?   788   1... ?

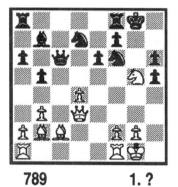 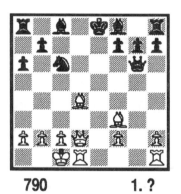 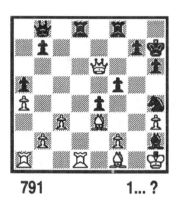

789   1. ?   790   1. ?   791   1... ?

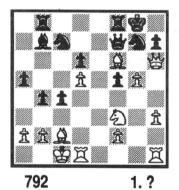 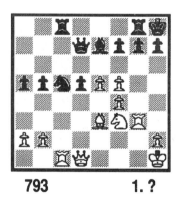 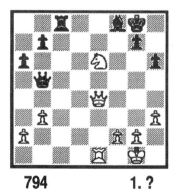

792   1. ?   793   1. ?   794   1. ?

CLEARANCE

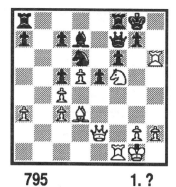

795   1. ?

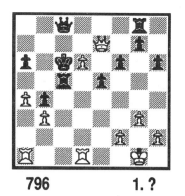

796   1. ?

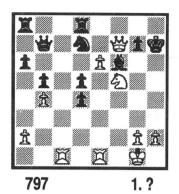

797   1. ?

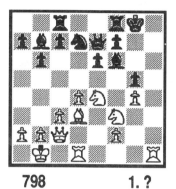

798   1. ?

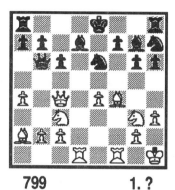

799   1. ?

800   1... ?

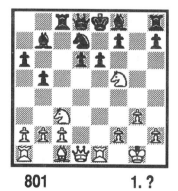

801   1. ?

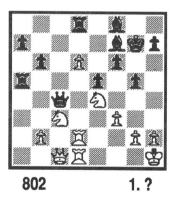

802   1. ?

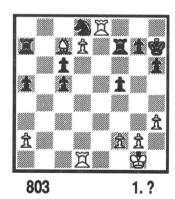

803   1. ?

CLEARANCE

157

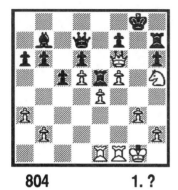

804   1. ?

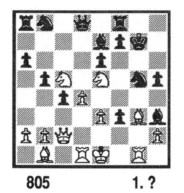

805   1. ?

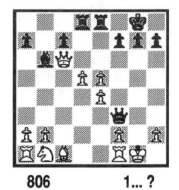

806   1... ?

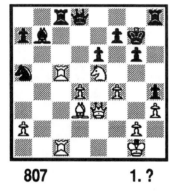

807   1. ?

CLEARANCE

750) 1...c4! 2.Bxc4 [2.Qxd4 exd4 and two pieces hang] **2...Qxc3+! 3.Kxc3 exf4+ 4.e5 Bxe5+** wins.

751) 1.Rxf6! Rxf6 [1..gxf6 2.Qg6+ and wins] **2.Rd8+ Kf7 3.Ng5+!! hxg5 4.Qe8#.**

752) 1.Qxd6!! Qxd6 2.Bc4+ Rf7 3.Bxf7+ Kf8 4.Bc5! hxg6 5.Bc4! and wins.

753) 1.e6!! exd3 [1...Bxe6 2.Bxg7+ Kxg7 3.Qd4+ Kf7 4.Bh5#] **2.Bxd3 Nf6 3.gxf6 Bxf6 4.Rxh7+ Kg8 5.Nxf6+** winning.

754) 1...Rxd3! 2.Bxd3 c4! 3.Qd6 Ne8! [3...cxd3? 4.Qxc6 Rxc6 5.Rb8+] **4.Qb4 Qxb4 5.cxb4 cxd3** and wins.

755) 1.Rd8+! [1...Bxd8 2.e7+].

756) 1.Rxd5! [1...exd5 2.e6+].

757) 1...Ra1+! 2.Nxa1 Ba2#.

758) 1.Bd5+! [1...exd5 2.Qh7#].

759) 1.Rxb6! axb6 2.Nf6+ winning. [2...Kf8 3.Qd6+].

760) 1.Qh4! Kg7 2.Nh5+! and wins. [2...gxh5 3.Qf6+ Kf8 4.Ne7#].

761) 1. Rc6+! [1...Bxc6 2.Nc5+ Ka5 3.Bc7#].

762) 1.Qxf5! followed by Ne6+.

763) 1.f3!! Qxf3 2.Qd1! winning. [2...Rxd6 3.Rh2+, or 2...Qh5 3.Rxd8].

764) 1...Bb5! 2.axb5 Nhg3+! 3.Nxg3 Nxg3+ 4.hxg3 hxg3+ 5.Kg1 Rh1+! 6.Kxh1 Rh8+ 7.Kg1 Bc5+! 8.Nxc5 Rh1+! 9.Kxh1 Qh8+ 10.Kg1 Qh2#.

765) 1...e3! 2.fxe3 dxe3 3.Nxe3 Nd3+! 4.exd3 Qxg3+ 5.Ke2 Nd4#.

766) 1...Qb8!! 2.dxc4 Ba3! 3.cxd5+ Kd7 4.Qxa3 Rh8+ 5.Kg1 Rh1+ 6.Kxh1 Rh8+ 7.Kg1 Rh1+! 8.Kxh1 Qh8+ 9.Kg1 Qh2+ 10.Kxf1 Qh1#.

767) 1...Qxh7 2.Rxh7 **Nd3+** and 3..Nxe1.

768) 1...Kg7 2.e6 Rh8+ 3.Kg1 Qe8 4.g4 Rh1+! 5.Kxh1 Qh8+ 6.Kg1 Qh3 mates.

769) 1...Ne2+ 2.Kh1 Qxg4! 3.hxg4 Rh5+! 4.gxh5 Rh4#.

770) 1.Bg5 Qxg5 2.Qf5+! Qxf5 3.Rxd8+ Kxd8 4.Re8#.

771) 1.Bxc4! e6 [1...Nxf5 2.Bxf7#] **2.Bb5+ Ke7** [2...Nd7 3.Bxd7+ Qxd7 4.Qf4] **3.Ng6+! hxg6 4.Nd5+! exd5 5.Qe5#.**

772) 1.Qd8+ Qf8 2.Rxh6+! Bxh6 3.Qf6+ Qg7 [3...Bg7 4.Rh1#] **4.Rh1! Qxf6 5.exf6** and mate next.

773) 1.Rh8+ Kxh8 2.Rh1+ Kg8 3.Rh8+! Kxh8 4.Qh1+ Kg8 5.Qh7#.

774) 1.Bxf7 Rxf7 [1...Qxf7 2.Qd8+] **2.Qh8#.**

775) 1.Ne5! Qe6 [1...Qe8 2.Nhg6+! hxg6 3.Bc4! bxc4 4.Rh1+ Kg8 5.Qxc4+ Rf7 6.Nxg6 and 7.Rh8#] **2.Bc4! bxc4 3.f5! Qxe5 4.Ng6+! hxg6 5.fxg6 Qxg5 6.Rh1+ Kg8 7.Qxc4+ Qd5 8.Rh8+! Kxh8 9.Qh4+ Kg8 10.Qh7#.**

776) 1.b5! Bxb5 2.Ne6! h5 3.Qf6+ Kh7 4.Bb4 and the threat 5.Ng5+ Kh6 6.Bf8+ wins.

777) 1.f4! exf4 2.Rxg6+ Kxg6 3.Qh5+ Kg7 4.Qh6+ Kg8 5.Qh8#.

778) 1.Ne5!! dxe5 [1...Qxe5 2.Qxe5 dxe5 3.g6 and 4.Rh8#] 2.g6! Qxg6 3.Qc4+ Qf7 4.Rh8#.

779) 1.Ne7+! Qxe7 2.Qxh7+! Kxh7 3.Rh5+ Kg8 4.Rh8#.

780) 1.Nd5! exd5 2.Rxf7+! Kxf7 3.Qxg6+ Kf8 4.Rf1+ Bf6 5.Rxf6+ winning easily.

781) 1.Re8+! Rxe8 2.Qg4+!! Qxg4 3.Nf6#.

782) 1.Re4! g5 2.Rh4+! gxh4 3.Qh6+ Rh7 4.Qxh7#.

783) 1.Rxb5! cxb5 2.Rc8! Qd5 [2...Rxc8 3.Qa1+! Kg8 4.Nh6# or 2...Qxc8 3.Qd4+ Kg8 4.Nh6#] 3.Qa1+! e5 4.Bxe5+ Qxe5 5.Rxf8+! Kg7 6.Rf7+! Kxf7 7.Nxe5+ or 6...Kg8 7.Qxa8+.

784) 1.Nd5! exd5 2.Bxd5+ Be6 3.Bxe6+ Qxe6 4.Rxg7+! Kxg7 5.Qh7+ Kf6 6.Rh6#.

785) 1.Bxh7+! Kxh7 2.Rh3+ Nh6 3.Nc4! dxc4 4.Bxh6 gxh6 5.Qh5 and wins.

786) 1.Nf5!! and wins! [1...Nxd7 2.Qh2+ Kg8 3.Qg3+ Kf7 4.Qg7#. On 1...exf5 comes 2.Qh2+ Kg8 3.Qg3+ Kh8 4.Qg7#. Finally, 1...Qb8 2.Rh7+! Nxh7 3.Qg7#].

787) 1.Qf6+! Nxf6 2.Bc5+ and wins. [2...Bxc5 3.gxf6+ Kf8 4.Rh8#].

788) 1...Qd1+!! 2.Rxd1 Ne2+!! 3.Bxe2 Nb3#.

789) 1.d5 Qxd5 2.Qh7+ Nxh7 3.Bxh7#.

790) 1.Bf6! Qxf6 2.Rhe1+ Be7 [2...Be6 3.Qd7#] **3.Bxc6+ Kf8 4.Qd8+! Bxd8 5.Re8#.**

791) 1...Bg1! 2.Kxg1 Nf3+!

792) 1.g6! Qxg6 [1...Qxf6 2.Qxh7# or 1...hxg6 2.Ng5!] **2.Bxg7 Qxg7 3.Rg1** wins.

793) 1.e6! fxe6 2.Ne5 Qe8 3.Ng6+! hxg6 4.Rh3+ Bh4 5.Rxh4#.

794) 1.Ng5! hxg5 2.Qe6+ and **3.Qxc8.**

795) 1.Ne7+! Qxe7 2.Rh8+! Kxh8 [2...Kf7 3.Qh5+ g6 4.Qxg6#] **3.Qh5+ Kg8 4.Qh7+ Kf7 5.Bg6#.**

796) 1.d7 Qd8 2.Qd6+ and 3.Qxc5.

797) 1.Re5! [threatening 2.Qh5+ Kg8 3.Ne7+! Bxe7 4.Qf7+ Kh8 5.Rh5#] **1...Rf8** [1...Bxe5 2.Qh5+ Kg8 3.Ne7+ Kf8 4.Qf7#] **2.Ne7! Rxf7 3.Rh5#.**

798) 1.Ba6! Bxa6 2.Nexg5 Rfd8 3.Rh8+! Bxh8 4.Qh7+ Kf8 5.Qxh8#.

799) 1.Rxd7! Kxd7 2.Be3! Qxe3 3.Rxf7+ Kd8 4.Qxe6 wins.

800) 1...Rxb4! 2.Nxb4 Bh2+ 3.Kf1 [3.Kh1 Nf2#] **3...Qb6!** and wins.

801) 1.Rxe6+! fxe6 2.Qh5#.

802) 1.Nxf6! Kxf6 2.Ne4+ Kg7 3.Rc2! Qa4 4.Qxg5+ Bg6 [4...Kh8 5.Qxd8 Qxc2 6.Qxf8+ Bg8 7.Qf6#] **5.Rc7+ Kg8** [5...Rd7 6.Nc3!] **6.Qxg6+! hxg6 7.Nf6+ Kh8 8.Rh7#.**

803) 1.Rxd8! Rxc7 2.Rh8+! Kxh8 3.d8=Q+.

804) 1.Qxe5! dxe5 2.Nf6+ and 3.Nxd7.

805) 1.Nc6! Nxc6 2.Qh7+ Nxh7 3.Be5+ Kh6 4.Bg7#.

806) 1...Re6!! and wins. [2.dxe6 Bf2+! 3.Rf2 Rd1+, or 2.Nd2 Qg4+ 3.Kh1 Rxc6 4.dxc6 Qf4].

807) 1.Nxg6! fxg6 2.Qe5+ Kh6 [2...Qf6 3.Rc7+] **3.Rc7 Rxc7 4.Rxc7 Rg8 5.Qh5+!!** and mates.

10. ATTRACTION

This device is usually employed to attract an enemy piece onto an unfavorable square. Sometimes this implies that the piece being so attracted is placed under attack. The actual attraction is usually accomplished by a forcing sacrifice. Often a sacrifice will attract the King, exposing it to attack. One of the most famous types of attraction occurs with the so called "Greek Gift" sacrifice of a Bishop at h7 (Bxh7ch, or with Black, Bxh2ch). The attraction motif occurs quite frequently and careful analysis is suggested.

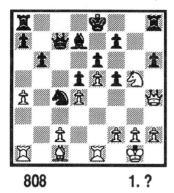
808   1. ?

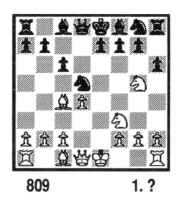
809   1. ?

810 ✓   1... ?

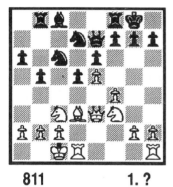
811   1. ?

812   1... ?

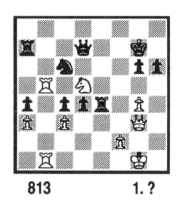
813   1. ?

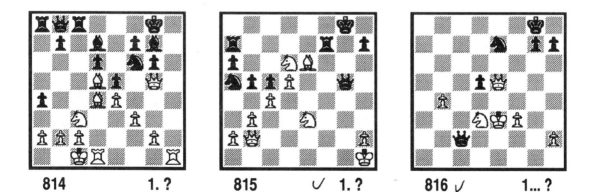
814   1. ?

815   ✓   1. ?

816 ✓   1... ?

ATTRACTION

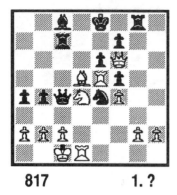

817　　　　　1. ?

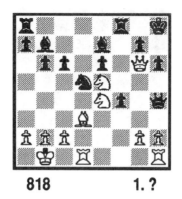

818　　　　　1. ?

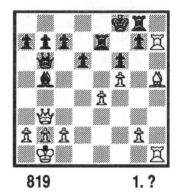

819　　　　　1. ?

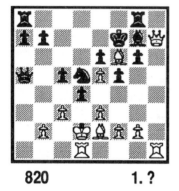

820　　　　　1. ?

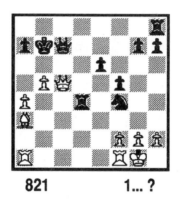

821　　　　　1... ?

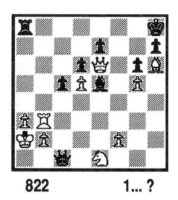

822　　　　　1... ?

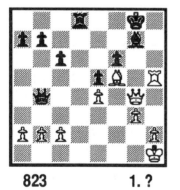

823　　　　　1. ?

824　　　　　1... ?

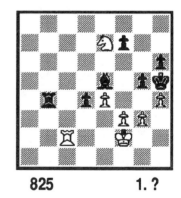

825　　　　　1. ?

ATTRACTION

826   1. ?

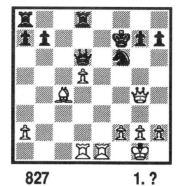

827   1. ?

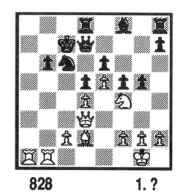

828   1. ?

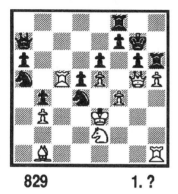

829   1. ?

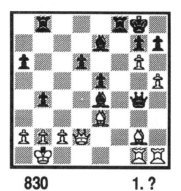

830   1. ?

831   1. ?

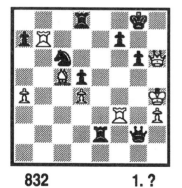

832   1. ?

833   1. ?

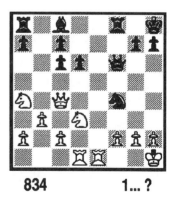

834   1... ?

ATTRACTION

808) 1.Nxf7 Kxf7 2.Qf6+ Kg8 3.Ra3! f4 [3...Be8 4.Rg3+ Kh7 5.Qh6#, or 3...Nxa3 4.Qg6+ Kf8 5.Bxa3+] **4.Bxf4 Nxa3 5.Re3 Be8 6.Rg3+** and wins.

809) 1.Nxf7!! Kxf7 2.Ne5+ Ke6 3.Qg4+ Kd6 4.Nf7+ winning.

810) 1...Bxg5+! 2.Kxg5 f6+ 3.Kg6 Qg4#.

811) 1.Bxh7+! Kxh7 2.Ng5+ Kg6 3.Qh3 Ndxe5 4.Qh7+ and wins [4...Kf6 5.Nce4+ dxe4 6.Nxe4#].

812) 1...Qd4+ 2.Bd3 Bc3+ 3.Ke2 [3.Nxc3 Qe3#, or 3.Kc1 Bxa1] **3...Qe3+!! 4.Nxe3 Nd4#.**

813) 1.Nf6!! Kxf6 2.Qf3+ Kg7 3.Qxe4 picking up the Rook.

814) 1.Rh8+! Kxh8 [1...Bxh8 2.Qxg6+] **2.Bxf7 Nh5 3.Qxg6** and wins.

815) 1.Bxf7+ Rxf7 2.Qh8+!! Kxh8 3.Nxf7+ with an extra piece after 4.Nxg5.

816) 1...d4+!! and wins. [2.Qxd4 Nf5+, or 2.Kxd4 Nc6+. If 2.Kf4 Ng6+, or 2.Ke4 Qe2+ 3.Kf4 Ng6+. On 2.Ke4 Qe2+ 3.Kf4 Ng6+ or 3.Kxd4 Nc6+].

817) 1.Bxe4 fxe4 2.Qd8+!! Kxd8 3.Nc6+ Ke8 4.Rd8#.

818) 1.Qh7+!! Kxh7 2.Nf6+ Kh8 3.Ng6#.

819) 1.Qxg8+ Kxg8 2.Rh8+ Kxh8 3.Bf7#.

820) 1.Qxg6+! Kxg6 2.Bh5+ Kh7 3.Bf7+ Bh6 4.Rxh6+ Kxh6 5.Rh1#.

821) 1...Ne2+! 2.Kh1 Qxh2+! and wins. [3.Kxh2 Rh4#].

822) 1...Rxa3+!! and mates!

823) 1.Rh8+!! Kxh8 [1...Kf7 2.Qg6+] 2.Qh5+ and wins. [2...Kg8 3.Be6+].

824) 1...Rh1+!! and mate next move.

825) 1.g4+! Kxh4 2.Kg2! and 3.Nf5# cannot be prevented.

826) 1.Qc4+! Qxc4 2.g8=Q+ winning the Black Queen.

827) 1.Re7+!! Qxe7 [1..Kxe7 2.Qxg7+ Ke8 3.Re1+] 2.d6+ Ke8 3.Bb5+ and wins. [3...Kf7 4.dxe7 Nxg4 5.exd8=Q].

828) 1.Rxb6!! gxf4 [1...Kxb6 2.Qa6+ Kc7 3.Ba5+ Nxa5 4.Qxa5+ Kc8 5.Qa8+ Kc7 6.Nxe6+! Qxe6 7.Ra7+ Kb6 8.Qb7#] 2.Qb5 Rb8 3.Rxb8 Nxb8 4.Ra7+.

829) 1.Qxh6+!! Kxh6 2.hxg6+ Kg7 3.Rh7+ Kg8 4.gxf7+ winning. [4...Rxf7 5.Rc8+].

830) 1.Qd5+!! and wins. [1..Bxd5 2.Bxd5+ Kh8 3.Rxg4].

831) 1.Bb6!! Qc6 [1...Nxb6 2.Qf4 Nd5 (2...Nf6 3.exf6+, or 2...Nxe5 3.Qh4#) 3.Qf7+ Kd8 4.Qe8#] 2.Nd5+!! exd5 3.Qb4+ Ke6 4.Qxg4+ and wins. 4...Ke7 5.Qh4+ Ke6 6.Qf4 with Qf7# to follow].

832) 1.Qg7+!! Kxg7 2.Rff7+ and mate in three to follow.

833) 1.Rxh6+! Kxh6 [1...gxh6 2.Rf7+ Kh8 3.Qf5] 2.g4!! winning. [2...g6 3.Rf7 with 4.Qh3# to follow, and on 3...Kg6 3.Bf7+ Kh6 4.Qh3#].

834) 1...Nxg2! 2. Kxg2 Bh3+!! 3.Kxh3 Qf3+ 4.Kh4 g5+! 5.Kxg5 Rf5+ 6.Kh4 Rh5#.

11. SMORGASBORD

Smorgasbord, according to Webster is defined as *"appetizers, served buffet style at a long table."* In this section we have prepared for you a sort of "chess smorgasbord" consisting of a potpourri of "mixed combinational appetizers served in a long chapter." These diagrams should prove entertaining if only because of their diverse qualities. Also, since the reader has not been given a direct hint as to the nature of the motif by a definitive chapter heading, we feel this will convey a more realistic, practical drill for over-the-board play. Continue to practice and review this book on a regular basis. Repetition is the key to recognizing these patterns when they occur in your games.

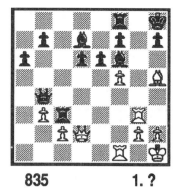

835   1. ?

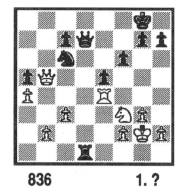

836   1. ?

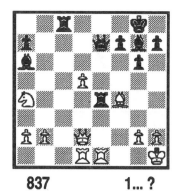

837   1... ?

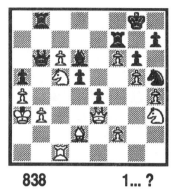

838   1... ?

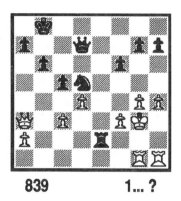

839   1... ?

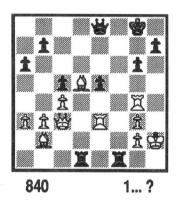

840   1... ?

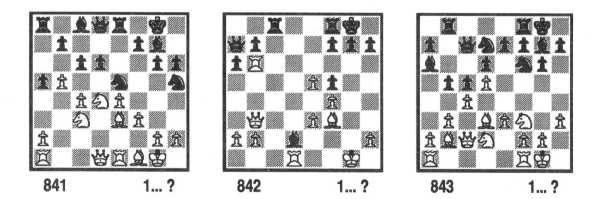

841   1... ?

842   1... ?

843   1... ?

SMORGASBORD

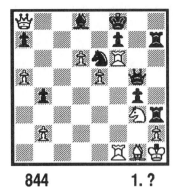

844   1. ?

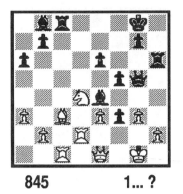

845   1... ?

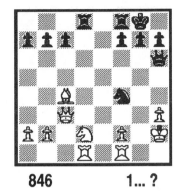

846   1... ?

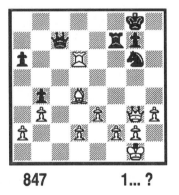

847   1... ?

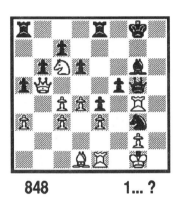

848   1... ?

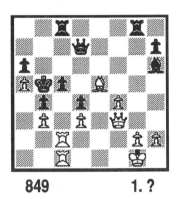

849   1. ?

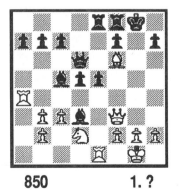

850   1. ?

851   1... ?

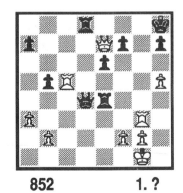

852   1. ?

SMORGASBORD

853   1... ?

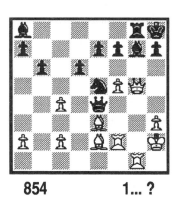

854   1... ?

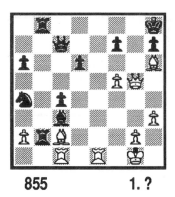

855   1. ?

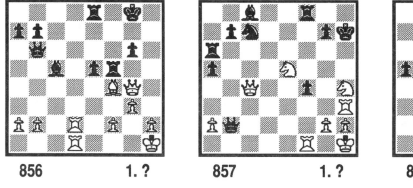

856   1. ?

857   1. ?

858   1. ?

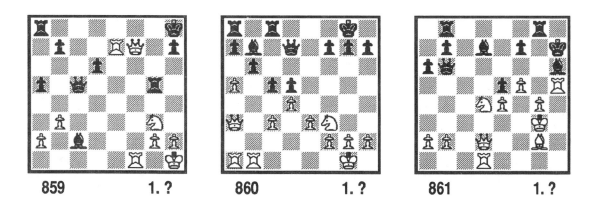

859   1. ?

860   1. ?

861   1. ?

SMORGASBORD

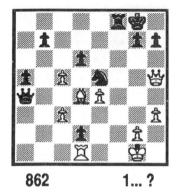

862   1... ?

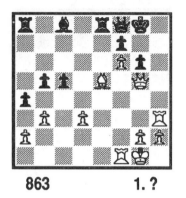

863   1. ?

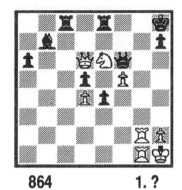

864   1. ?

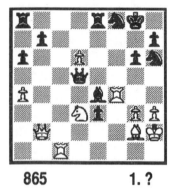

865   1. ?

866   1. ?

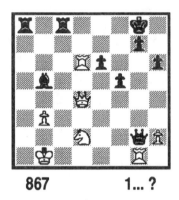

867   1... ?

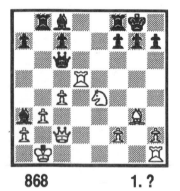

868   1. ?

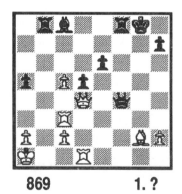

869   1. ?

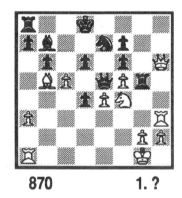

870   1. ?

SMORGASBORD

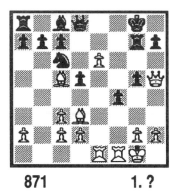

871   1. ?

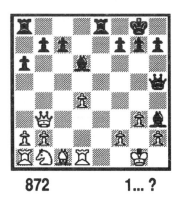

872   1... ?

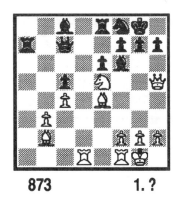

873   1. ?

874   1. ?

875   1. ?

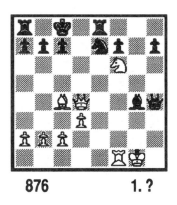

876   1. ?

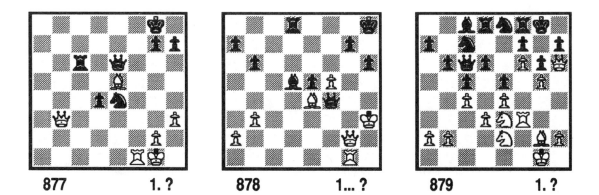

877   1. ?

878   1... ?

879   1. ?

SMORGASBORD

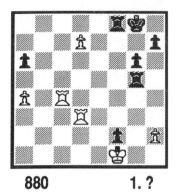

880   1. ?

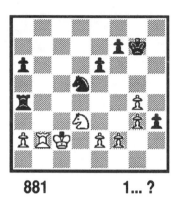

881   1... ?

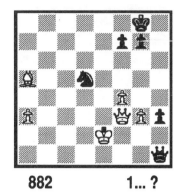

882   1... ?

883   1... ?

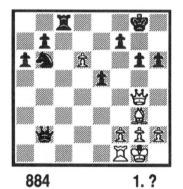

884   1. ?

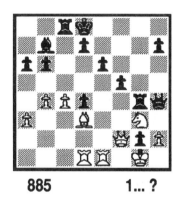

885   1... ?

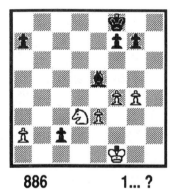

886   1... ?

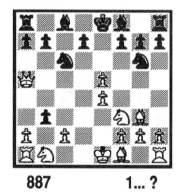

887   1... ?

888   1. ?

SMORGASBORD

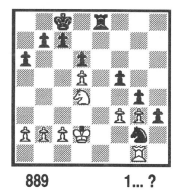

889   1... ?

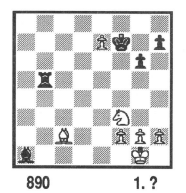

890   1. ?

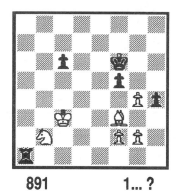

891   1... ?

892   1... ?

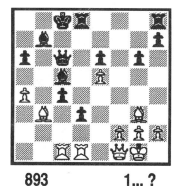

893   1... ?

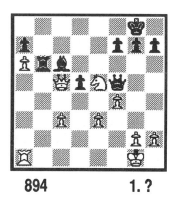

894   1. ?

895   1... ?

896   1... ?

897   1... ?

SMORGASBORD

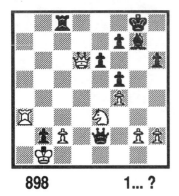

898   1... ?

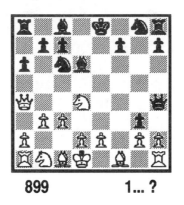

899   1... ?

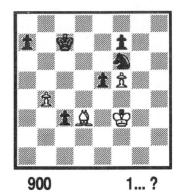

900   1... ?

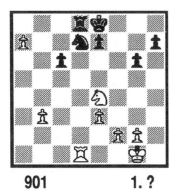

901   1. ?

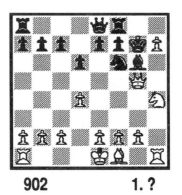

902   1. ?

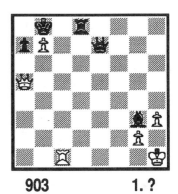

903   1. ?

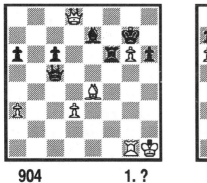

904   1. ?

905   1. ?

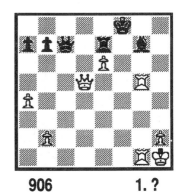

906   1. ?

SMORGASBORD

178

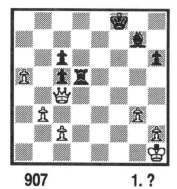
907   1. ?

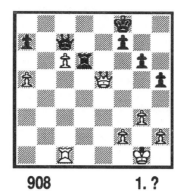
908   1. ?

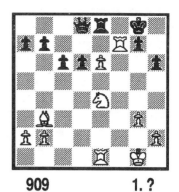
909   1. ?

910   1. ?

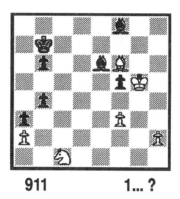
911   1... ?

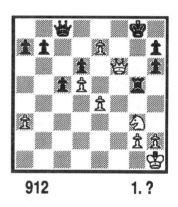
912   1. ?

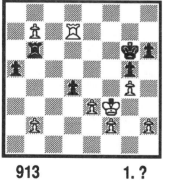
913   1. ?

914   1. ?

915   1... ?

SMORGASBORD

179

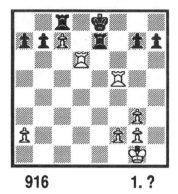

916   1. ?

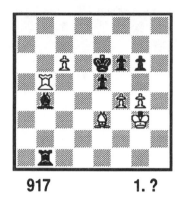

917   1. ?

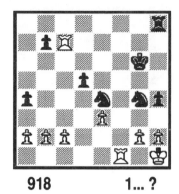

918   1... ?

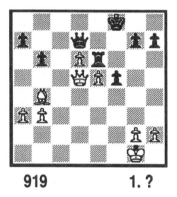

919   1. ?

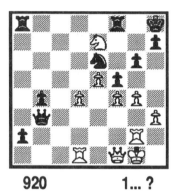

920   1... ?

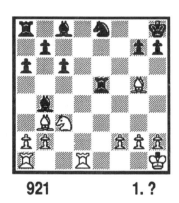

921   1. ?

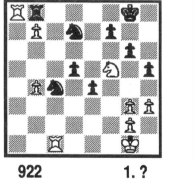

922   1. ?

923   1. ?

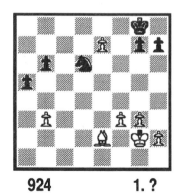

924   1. ?

SMORGASBORD

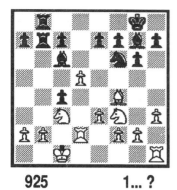

925   1... ?

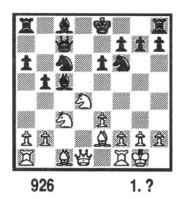

926   1. ?

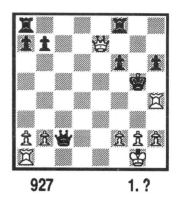

927   1. ?

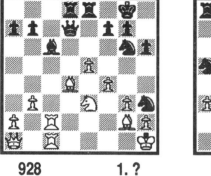

928   1. ?

929   1. ?

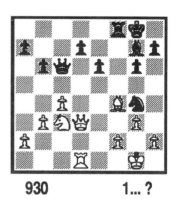

930   1... ?

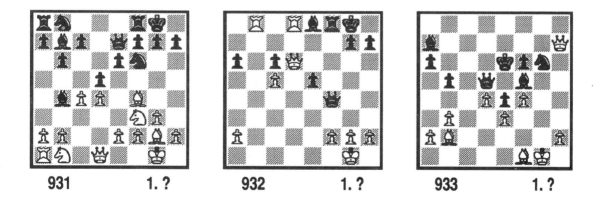

931   1. ?

932   1. ?

933   1. ?

SMORGASBORD

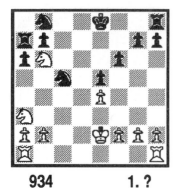

934   1. ?

935   1... ?

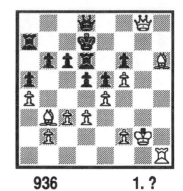

936   1. ?

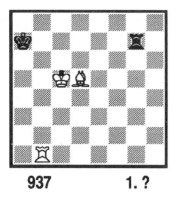

937   1. ?

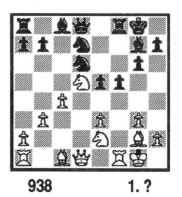

938   1. ?

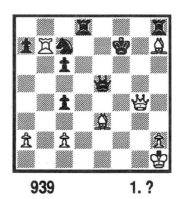

939   1. ?

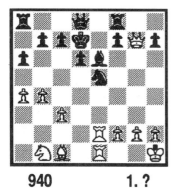

940   1. ?

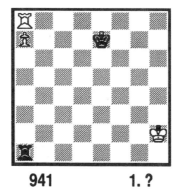

941   1. ?

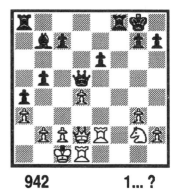

942   1... ?

SMORGASBORD

943   1. ?

944   1. ?

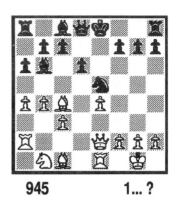

945   1... ?

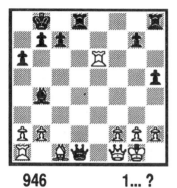

946   1... ?

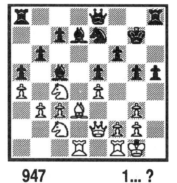

947   1... ?

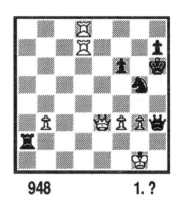

948   1. ?

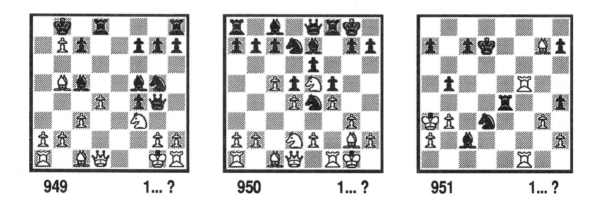

949   1... ?

950   1... ?

951   1... ?

SMORGASBORD

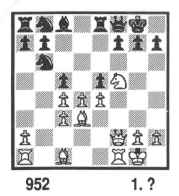

952   1. ?

953   1... ?

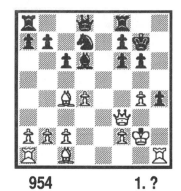

954   1. ?

955   1... ?

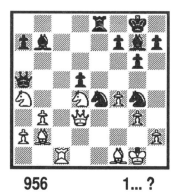

956   1... ?

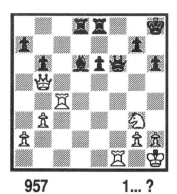

957   1... ?

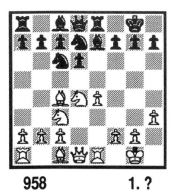

958   1. ?

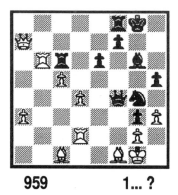

959   1... ?

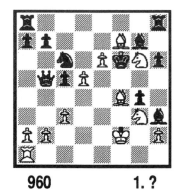

960   1. ?

SMORGASBORD

961   1... ?

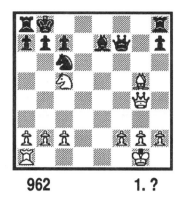

962   1. ?

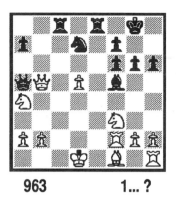

963   1... ?

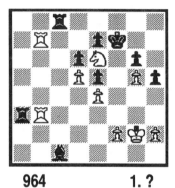

964   1. ?

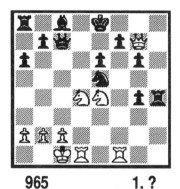

965   1. ?

966   1. ?

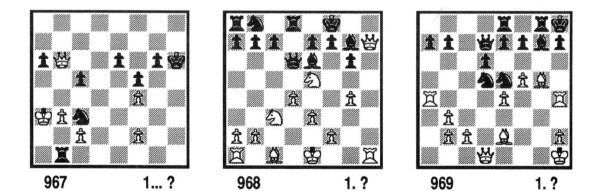

967   1... ?

968   1. ?

969   1. ?

SMORGASBORD

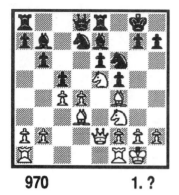

970   1. ?

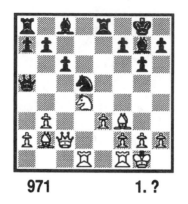

971   1. ?

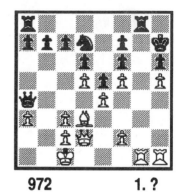

972   1. ?

973   1. ?

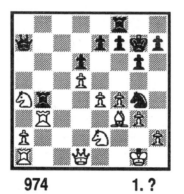

974   1. ?

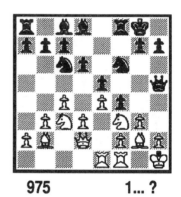

975   1... ?

976   1. ?

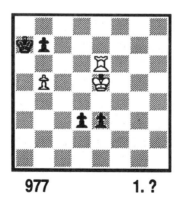

977   1. ?

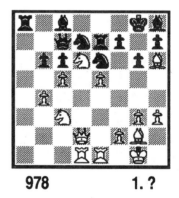

978   1. ?

SMORGASBORD

979   1. ?

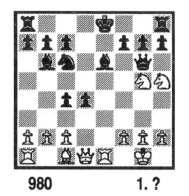

980   1. ?

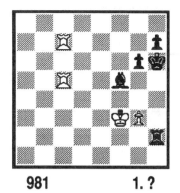

981   1. ?

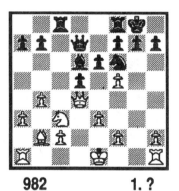

982   1. ?

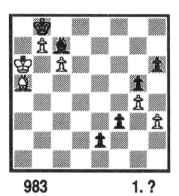

983   1. ?

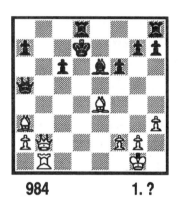

984   1. ?

985   1. ?

986   1... ?

987   1. ?

SMORGASBORD

187

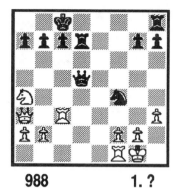

988   1. ?

989   1... ?

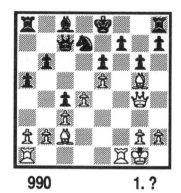

990   1. ?

991   1... ?

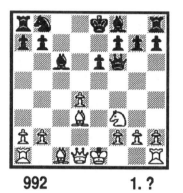

992   1. ?

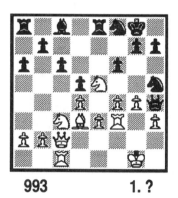

993   1. ?

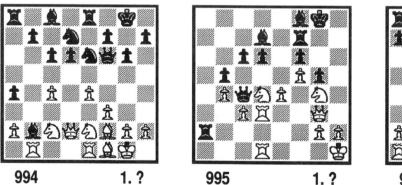

994   1. ?

995   1. ?

996   1. ?

SMORGASBORD

188

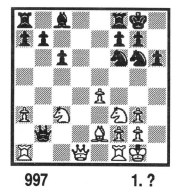

997   1. ?

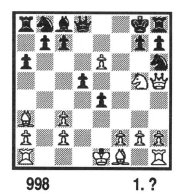

998   1. ?

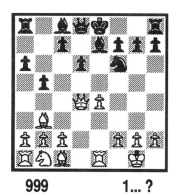

999   1... ?

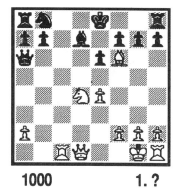

1000   1. ?

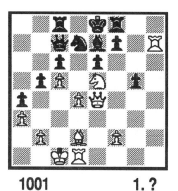

1001   1. ?

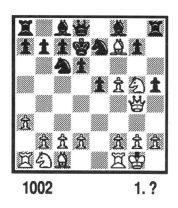

1002   1. ?

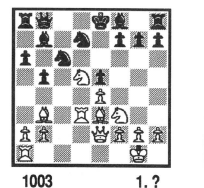

1003   1. ?

1004   1. ?

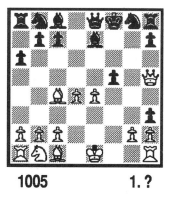

1005   1. ?

SMORGASBORD

1006　　　　1. ?

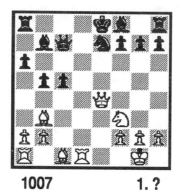

1007　　　　1. ?

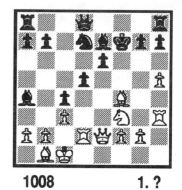

1008　　　　1. ?

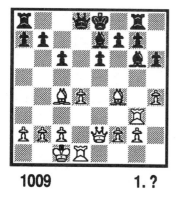

1009　　　　1. ?

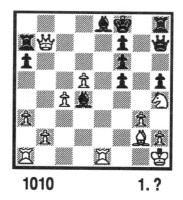

1010　　　　1. ?

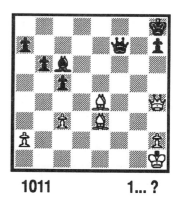

1011　　　　1... ?

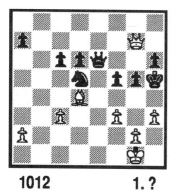

1012　　　　1. ?

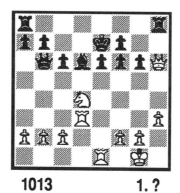

1013　　　　1. ?

1014　　　　1. ?

SMORGASBORD

1015   1. ?

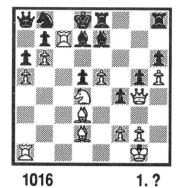

1016   1. ?

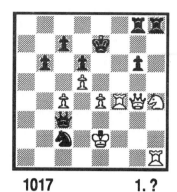

1017   1. ?

1018   1. ?

1019   1... ?

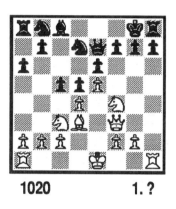

1020   1. ?

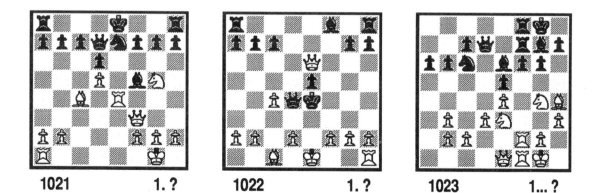

1021   1. ?

1022   1. ?

1023   1... ?

SMORGASBORD

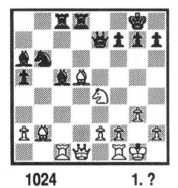

1024   **1. ?**

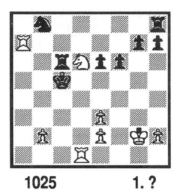

1025   **1. ?**

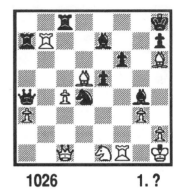

1026   **1. ?**

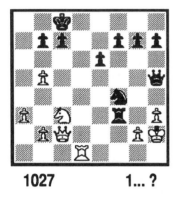

1027   **1... ?**

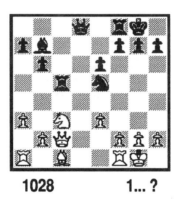

1028   **1... ?**

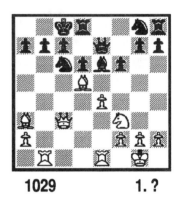

1029   **1. ?**

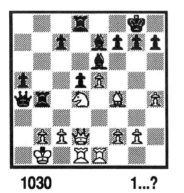

1030   **1...?**

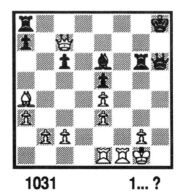

1031   **1... ?**

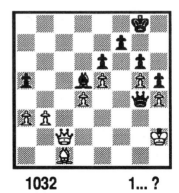

1032   **1... ?**

SMORGASBORD

192

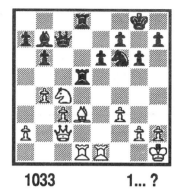

1033   1... ?

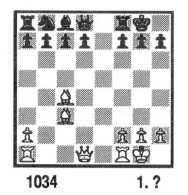

1034   1. ?

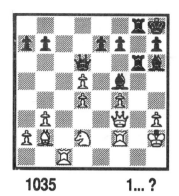

1035   1... ?

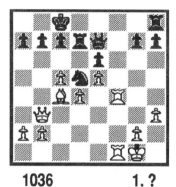

1036   1. ?

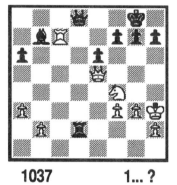

1037   1... ?

1038   1... ?

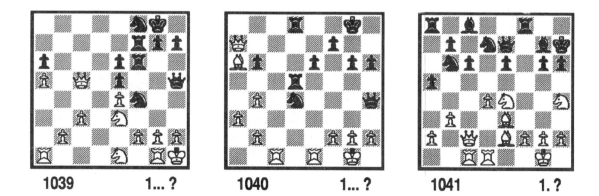

1039   1... ?

1040   1... ?

1041   1. ?

SMORGASBORD

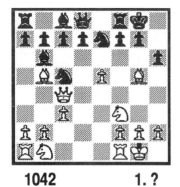

1042 1. ?	1043 1... ?	1044 1... ?

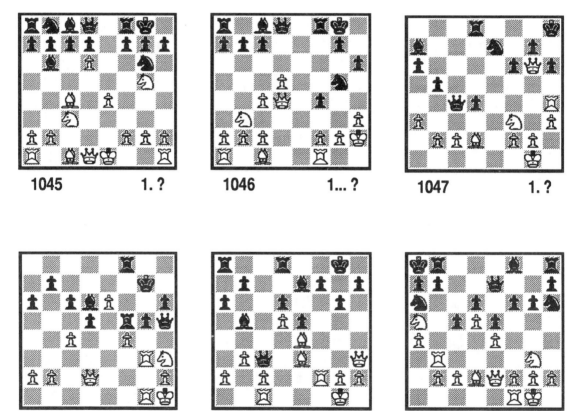

1045 1. ?	1046 1... ?	1047 1. ?

1048 1. ?	1049 1. ?	1050 1. ?

SMORGASBORD

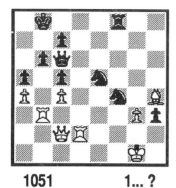

1051   1... ?

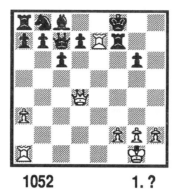

1052   1. ?

1053   1. ?

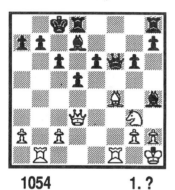

1054   1. ?

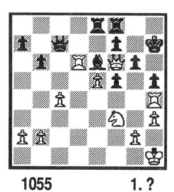

1055   1. ?

1056   1. ?

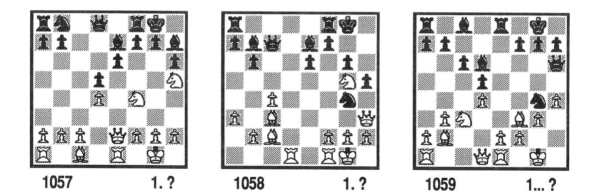

1057   1. ?   1058   1. ?   1059   1... ?

SMORGASBORD

1060   1. ?

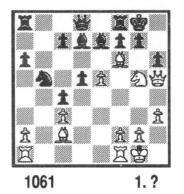

1061   1. ?

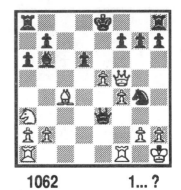

1062   1... ?

1063   1. ?

1064   1... ?

1065   1. ?

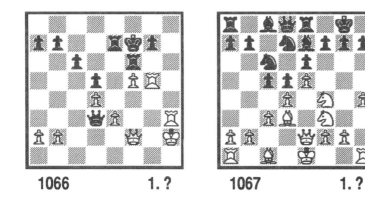

1066   1. ?

1067   1. ?

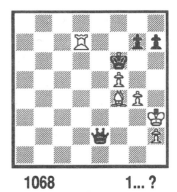

1068   1... ?

SMORGASBORD

196

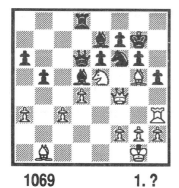

1069   1. ?

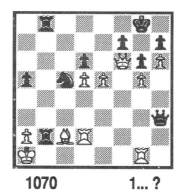

1070   1... ?

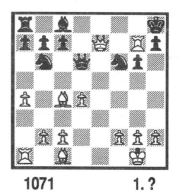

1071   1. ?

1072   1. ?

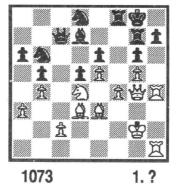

1073   1. ?

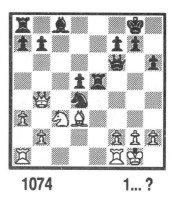

1074   1... ?

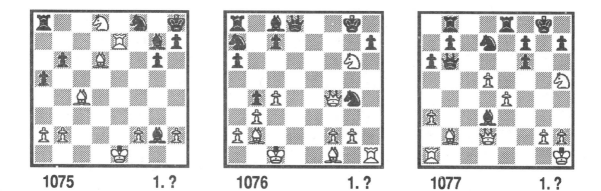

1075   1. ?

1076   1. ?

1077   1. ?

SMORGASBORD

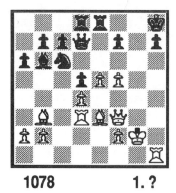

1078   1. ?

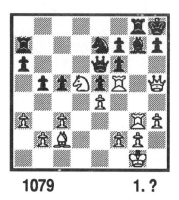

1079   1. ?

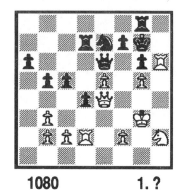

1080   1. ?

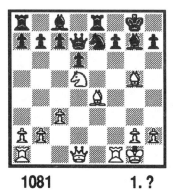

1081   1. ?

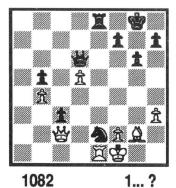

1082   1... ?

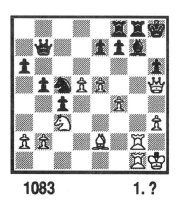

1083   1. ?

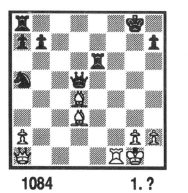

1084   1. ?

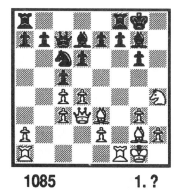

1085   1. ?

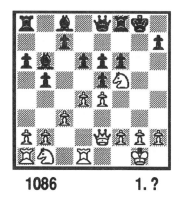

1086   1. ?

SMORGASBORD

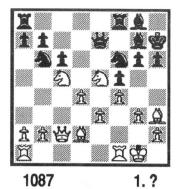

1087   1. ?

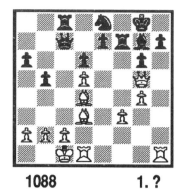

1088   1. ?

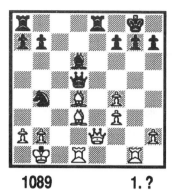

1089   1. ?

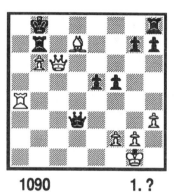

1090   1. ?

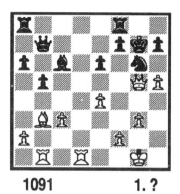

1091   1. ?

1092   1...?

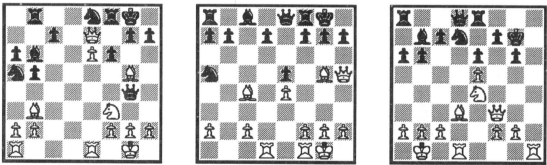

1093   1. ?

1094   1. ?

1095   1. ?

SMORGASBORD

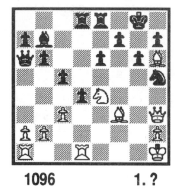

1096   1. ?

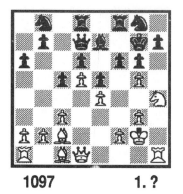

1097   1. ?

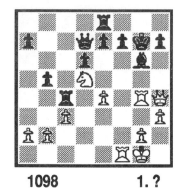

1098   1. ?

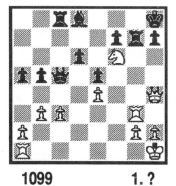

1099   1. ?

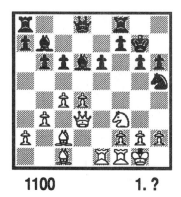

1100   1. ?

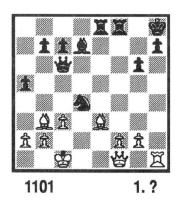

1101   1. ?

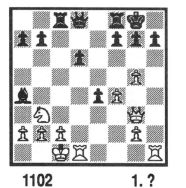

1102   1. ?

1103   1... ?

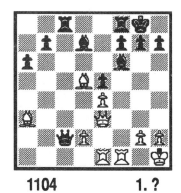

1104   1. ?

SMORGASBORD

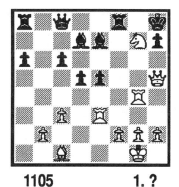

1105   1. ?

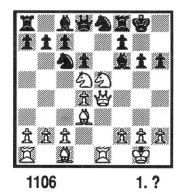

1106   1. ?

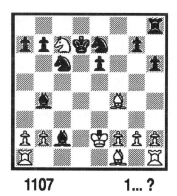

1107   1... ?

1108   1. ?

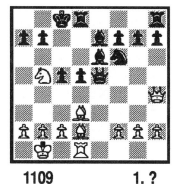

1109   1. ?

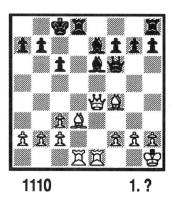

1110   1. ?

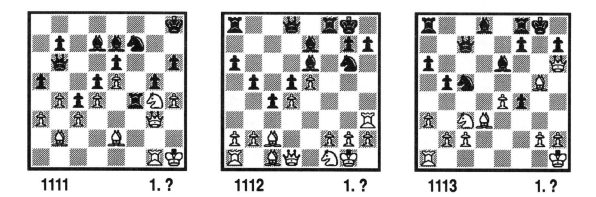

1111   1. ?

1112   1. ?

1113   1. ?

SMORGASBORD

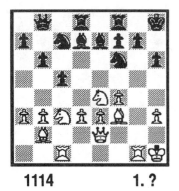

1114   1. ?

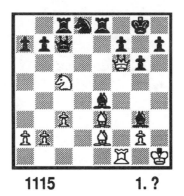

1115   1. ?

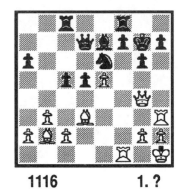

1116   1. ?

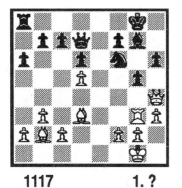

1117   1. ?

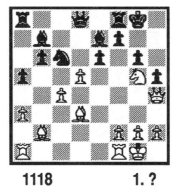

1118   1. ?

1119   1... ?

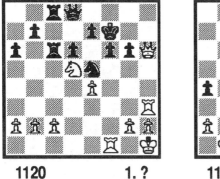

1120   1. ?

1121   1. ?

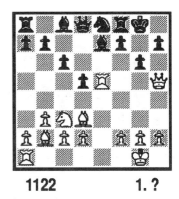

1122   1. ?

SMORGASBORD

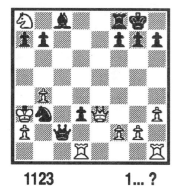

1123   1... ?

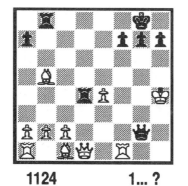

1124   1... ?

1125   1. ?

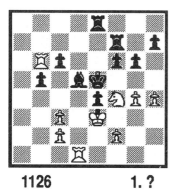

1126   1. ?

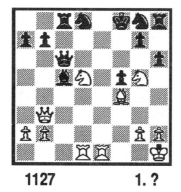

1127   1. ?

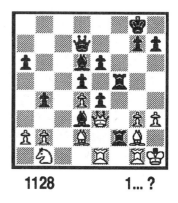

1128   1... ?

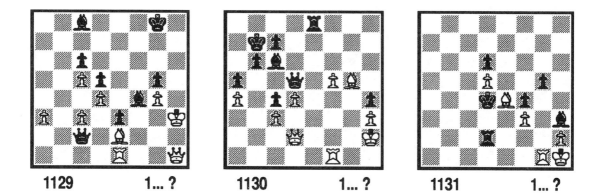

1129   1... ?

1130   1... ?

1131   1... ?

SMORGASBORD

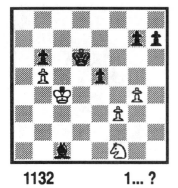

1132   1... ?

1133   1... ?

1134   1. ?

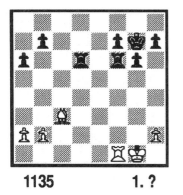

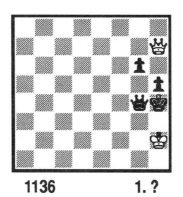

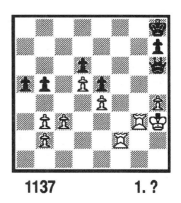

1135   1. ?

1136   1. ?

1137   1. ?

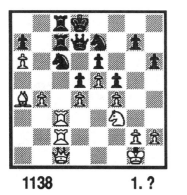

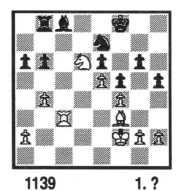

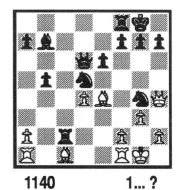

1138   1. ?

1139   1. ?

1140   1... ?

SMORGASBORD

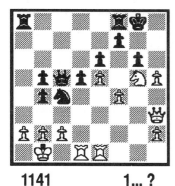

1141　　　　1... ?

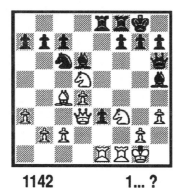

1142　　　　1... ?

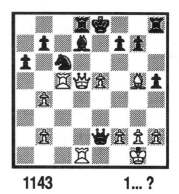

1143　　　　1... ?

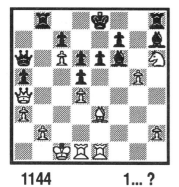

1144　　　　1... ?

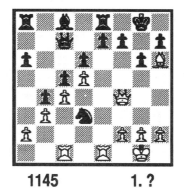

1145　　　　1. ?

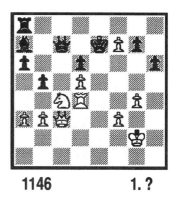

1146　　　　1. ?

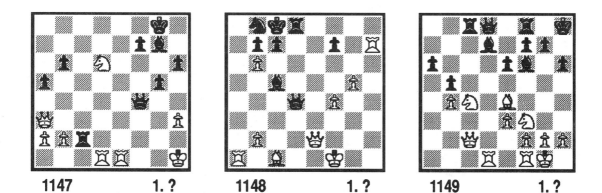

1147　　　　1. ?

1148　　　　1. ?

1149　　　　1. ?

SMORGASBORD

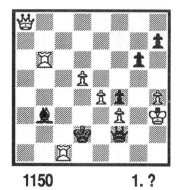

1150   1. ?

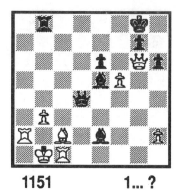

1151   1... ?

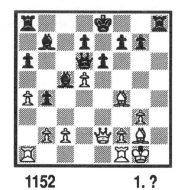

1152   1. ?

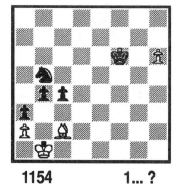

1153   1. ?

1154   1... ?

SMORGASBORD

206

835) 1.Qh6 Rxg3 2.Bg6!! Rxg6 3.fxg6 fxg6 4.Qxf8#.

836) 1.Nd4! f5 [1...exd4 2.Qb3+ picking up the Rook] **2.Nxc6** winning [2...fxe4 3.Qb8+ Kf7 4.Nxe5+].

837) 1...Rc2! 2.Qa5 [2.Qxc2 Rxe1+ mates] **2...Bc3! 3.Rxe4 Qxe4 4.Qd8+ Kg7 5.Rg1 Bd4 6.Bd6 Qxg2+! 7.Rxg2 Rc1+ 8.Rg1 Rxg1#.**

838) 1...d4! 2.Qxd4 Qxb3#.

839) 1...Qd6+ 2.Kh3 Nf4+ 3.Kg3 Nh5+-+ 4.Kh3 Qg3+ 5.Rxg3 Nf4#.

840) 1...Qf7!! 2.Bxf7+ Kf8 and White cannot prevent the Rook from mating on h1.

841) 1...c5! 2.Nde2 [2.Nc2 Nxf3+ 3.gxf3 Bxc3] **2...Nxc4** wins a pawn.

842) 1...Rc3! 2.bxc3 Bxe3+ and 3...Bxb6 wins a pawn.

843) 1...bxc4 2.bxc4 (2.Nxc4 Nxd5; or 2.Bxc4 Bxc4 don't change things) **2...Rxb2! 3.Qxb2 Nxd5! 4.Qa3 Bxa1 5.Rxa1** [5.Qxa6 5...Nb4! and the Ba1 escapes] **5...Nb4!** and Black has won a pawn.

844) 1.Rxe6 Qh4 2.Rf2 Rxg3 3.Re7! and 4.Qxd8 wins.

845) 1...f2+ 2.Qxf2 [2.Rxf2 Bxg3! 3.hxg3 Rh1#] **2...Rxh2! 3.Qxh2 Bxg3 4.Qe2** [4.Qh3 Qxe3+ 5.Kf1 Rxc3! wins] **4...Bf4+ 5.Kf1 Bxe3 6.Qh2** [6.Ke1 Qg3+] **6...Bxd4** winning.

846) 1...Rd3! 2.Qxd3 [2.Bxd3 Qxh3+ 3.Kg1 Qg2#] **2...Nxd3 3.Bxd3 Qd6+** and 4...Qxd3.

847) 1...Nf4! 2.exf4 [if the Rd6 moves then 2...Ne7+ wins the Queen] **2...Qxd6.**

848) 1...Ne2+ 2.Bxe2 [2.Rxe2 Qxg4] **2...Qxe3+ and 3...fxg4.**

849) 1.Bc7!! Qxc7 [or 1...Rxc7 2.Qb7+! Rxb7 3.Rxc5#] **2.Rxc5+! Qxc5 3.Qb7+ Kxa5 4.Ra1#.**

850) 1.Ne4! Bxe4 2.Rxe4 dxe4 3.Qg3#.

851) 1...Bd6!! 2.Rxd6 [2.Bxd6 d1=Q] **h2** and queens a pawn.

852) 1.Rd5! exd5 [1...Qxd5 2.Qf6#] **2.Qxd8+ Re8 3.Qxe8#.**

853) 1...Be3!! 2.Qxe3 [or 2.Bxe3 h3! 3.g3 Qf3 mating. Of course not 2.fxe3 Qxg2#] **2...Rxe3 3.fxe3 h3 4.Rf2 Qd1+ 5.Rf1 h2+ 6.Kf2 Qxf1+! 7.Kxf1 h1=Q+** wins.

854) 1...Ng4+! followed by 2...Be5+ wins the White Queen.

855) 1.Re5! [not 1.f6 Qc5+] **1...Bxe5** [1...dxe5 2.Qg7#] **2.f6 Bxf6 3.Qxf6+** and mate next.

856) 1.Rd6! Bxd6 2.Qxg6+ Kh8 [2...Kf8 3.Qxf5+] **3.Qxe8+ Rf8 4.Bxe5+!** and wins.

857) 1.Qe6!! Bxe6 [1...Nxe6 2.Nhg6+ mates and 1...Rxe6 2.Nhg6+ Kg8 3.Rh8#] **2.Nf5+ Kg8 3.Ne7#.**

858) 1.Re3! Bxe3 2.Qxg7#.

859) 1.Nf5! Bxf5 2.Qf6+ Kg8 3.Qxg5+ Bg6 4.Qf6 and mates.

860) 1.a6! Bc6 2.dxc5 bxc5 3.Qxc5 wins a pawn.

861) **1.Ne6!** and 2.Qxh6#.

862) **1...Nf3+ 2.gxf3 Qxd1+** wins.

863) **1.Qxg6+ fxg6 2.f7+ Qxf7 3.Rh8#.**

864) **1.Nf8 Rxf8** [1...Qxd6 2.Rg8# or 1...Qxf8 2.Rg8+ Qxg8 3.Qf6+ mates] **2.Rg8+ Rxg8 3.Qxf6+ Rg7 4.Qxg7#.**

865) **1.Rc7! Ne6** [1...Nf5 2.Rxf5] **2.Rxe4** wins.

866) **1.e7! Rf7** [if 1...Rfe8 then 2.Rxg7+! Kxg7 3.Rg1+ and mates, or 1...Qxe7 2.Qxd5+ Kh8 3.Kxb2 wins] **2.Rxg7+! Kxg7** [2...Rxg7 3.e8=Q+] **3.Rg1+** and mates quickly.

867) **1...Bd3+! 2.Qxd3 Qxg1+.**

868) **1.Bd6! Bxd6 2.Nf6+! gxf6 3.Rg1+ Kh8 4.Qxh7+ Kxh7 5.Rh5#.**

869) **1.Rg3+ Kf7 2.Qxf4+.**

870) **1.Ne6+! fxe6 2.Qf8+ Kc7 3.Qxe7+ Kb8 4.Rh8+ Bc8 5.Rxc8+ Kxc8 6.Ba6+** and mate next.

871) **1.e7! Nxe7 2.Bxe7 Rxe7 3.Qxg5+ Kf8 4.Rxf4+ Ke8 5.Qg8+ Kd7 6.Bf5+** winning.

872) **1...Re3!! 2.fxe3** [2.Qxe3 Qxd1+ mates, while 2.Bxe3 loses to 2...Qf3] **2...Qe2 3.Qxb7 Qxd1+ 4.Kf2 Qf1#.**

873) **1.Rd7! Bxd7 2.Bh7+! Nxh7** [2...Kh8 3.Nxf7#] **3.Qxf7+ Kh8 4.Ng6#.**

874) **1.Rf5! exf5 2.Qxh5#.**

875) **1.Be4! Bxe4** [1...Rxe4 2.h3+ Kg3 3.Rf3#] **2.h3+ Kg3 3.Be1#.**

876) **1.Be6+! Kb8** [1...fxe6 2.Qd7+ Kb8 3.Qxe8#] **2.Nd7+ Kc8 3.Nc5+ Kb8 4.Na6+ bxa6 5.Qb4#.**

877) **1.Bd6! Rxd6** [1...Qxb3 2.Rf8#] **2.Qxb8+** mates in two.

878) **1...g5! 2.fxg6 e.p. Bxe4** winning.

879) **1.Nf5!** [1...gxf5 2.Rh3 winning, or 1...Bxf5 2.exf5 gxf5 3.Rh3 with the same result].

880) **1.Rf3! Rd5 2.Rc8!** and wins.

881) **1...Rc4+ 2.Kd2 Rc1!** winning. [3.Kxc1 h2 and promotes].

882) **1...Qxf3+ 2.Kxf3 Ne3!** and wins. [3.Kxe3 h2].

883) **1...Rxg1+! 2.Kxg1 e2 3.Rf1 exf1=Q+** and wins.

884) **1.Qxc8+! Nxc8 2.d7** and queens next.

885) **1...Qxh2+! 2.Kxh2 Rh4+ 3.Kg1 Rh1+! 4.Nxh1 gxh1=Q#.**

886) **1...Bb2! 2.Nxb2 c1=Q+** and wins.

887) **1...b2! 2.Qc3 Bb4! 3.Qxb4 Nxb4** and 4...bxa1=Q.

888) **1.Rxg4! Rxg4 2.e7 Rg8 3.Rd8** and wins.

889) **1...Re1! 2.Rxe1 Nxe1 3.Kxe1 h2** and queens.

890) 1.e8=Q+! Kxe8 2.Ba4 wins.

891) 1...Ra3+ 2.Kc2 Rxf3! 3.gxf3 h3 and queens in two.

892) 1...f1=N+! 2.Kg1 Ng3+ 3.Rxe1 Rxe1+ 4.Kh2 Nf1+ 5.Kh1 Ne3+ 6.Rg1 Rxg1+ 7.Kxg1 Nxc4 wins.

893) 1...cxb3!! 2.Rxc5 Qxc5 3.Rc1 Qc2! and now if 4.Rxc2, then 4...dxc2 and 5...Rd1 queens.

894) 1.Qxb6! axb6 2.Nxc6 and the a-pawn will be decisive.

895) 1...Qe7!! 2.fxe7 Bg7 3.Qxb2 Bxb2 and 4...Bxa1 wins.

896) 1...Rxh7! 2.Rb1 [2.Rxh7 b1=Q] 2...Kc3 and 3...Kc2 wins.

897) 1...Qxf1+! 2.Qxf1 Re1+.

898) 1...Rxc2! 2.Nxc2 Qf1+ 3.Ka2 b1=Q#.

899) 1...Qxh2! 2.Rxh2 gxh2 and queens next.

900) 1...e4+! 2.Bxe4 Nxe4 3.Kxe4 c2.

901) 1.Rxd7! Kxd7 2.Nc5+ Ke8 [2...Kc7 3.Ne6+ or 2...Kd6 3.Nb7+] 3.Ne6! Rd1+ 4.Kh2 Ra1 5.a8=Q+ Rxa8 6.Nc7+ wins.

902) 1.h8=Q+ Rxh8 2.Nf5+ Kg8 3.Rxh8+ Kxh8 4.Qh6+ Kg8 5.Qg7#.

903) 1.Rc8+! Rxc8 2.Qxa7+! Kxa7 3.bxc8=N+ and 4.Nxe7 wins.

904) 1.Qh8+ Kxh8 2.g7+ Kg8 3.Bh7+ Kxh7 4.g8=Q#.

905) **1.Rc8! Rxc8 2.Re8+! Nxe8 3.d7! Nd6 4.dxc8=Q Nxc8 5.axb7** and queens on b8 or c8 next.

906) **1.Rxg7 Rxg7 2.Rxg7 Kxg7** [2...Qxg7 3.Qd8#] **3.Qd7+! Qxd7 4.exd7** and queens.

907) **1.Qxd5! cxd5 2.a6** and queens in two more moves.

908) **1.Qxd6+! Qxd6 2.c7** and wins.

909) **1.Rf8+! Kh7** [1...Rxf8 2.e7+ wins, or if 1...Kxf8 then 2.Rf1+ Kg8 (2...Ke7 3.Rf7#) 3.e7+ wins] **2.e7! Qxe7 3.Rxe8 Qxe8 4.Nf6+** and 5.Rxe8.

910) **1.Nh5! hxg6** [1...Nxh5 2.gxh7] **2.Nxf6 Kxf6 3.h7 Kg7 4.c5!** and queens a pawn.

911) **1...Bxa2! 2.Nxa2 b3 3.Nc3** [3.Nc1 b2 and queens] **3...b2 and 4...a2** queens by force.

912) **1.Qe6+! Qxe6 2.dxe6** and the e-pawn queens.

913) **1.Rd6+! Rxd6 2.b8=Q.**

914) **1.Qb5! Qxb5 2.c8=Q+ Kf7 3.Qxe6+! Kxe6 4.Nc7+** and 5.Nxb5.

915) **1...d2!** and now 2.Rd1 Qxe6 or 2.Qxd7 dxe1=Q#.

916) **1.Rd8+! Rxd8 2.Rf8+ Kxf8 3.cxd8=Q+.**

917) **1.f5+ gxf5 2.gxf5+ Kd6 3.Rxb4! Rxb4 4.Bc5+! Kxc5 5.c7.**

918) **1...Ng3+! 2.hxg3 hxg3+ 3.Kg1 Nf2 4.Rxf2 Rh1+!! 5.Kxh1 gxf2** promoting.

919) 1.Qxe6 Qxe6 2.d7+.

920) 1...Qxd1 2.Qxd1 a1=Q winning.

921) 1.f4! Re3 2.f5! Re5 3.Rd8! Ba5 4.f6! Bxd8 [4...gxf6 5.Bxf6#] **5.f7!** queens.

922) 1.Ne3! Nd6 [1...Nxe3 2.Rc8+] **2.Rc8+!! Nxc8 3.Rxb8 Nxb8 4.bxc8=Q+.**

923) 1.Qxh6+! gxh6 2.g7+ Kh7 3.gxf8=N+ Kh8 4.Rg8#.

924) 1.Bc4+ Kh8 [1...Nxc4 2.e8=Q+] **2.Bb5! Nxb5 3.e8=Q#.**

925) 1...Nxd5! 2.Nxd5 Bxd5 3.Rxd5 Rxb2 [threatening 4...Rb1+ 5.Kd2 R(b8)b2#] **4.Nd2 Rxa2 5.Nxc4 Ra1+ and 6...Rxh1** wins.

926) 1.Nxc6 Qxc6 2.Bf3 Nd5 3.Nxd5 exd5 4.Bxd5 wins a Rook.

927) 1.Qg7+ Kxh4 [if 1...Qg6 then 2.Rg4+! Kxg4 3.Qxg6+] **2.Qxh6+ Kg4 3.h3+ Kf5 4.Qh7+** and after the King moves, 5.Qxc2.

928) 1.Rxc6! bxc6 2.Bxc6 Qxd4 3.Qxd4 Rxd4 4.Bxe8 winning a pawn.

929) 1.Rc7! Qxc7 2.Qh7+ Bg7 3.Qxg7+ Ke6 4.Qxc7.

930) 1...g5! 2.f3 [2.Bxg5 Nxf2 or 2.Be3 Ne5 wins] **2...Qc5+! 3.Kg2 Qf2+ 4.Kh3 Qxh2+ 5.Kxg4 Rxf4+! 6.gxf4 Qh4#.**

931) 1.c5! [threatening 2.a3 Ba5 3.b4 trapping the Bishop] **1...bxc5 2.a3 Ba5 3.dxc5 c6** [3...Qxc5 4.b4] **4.Bd6** wins the exchange.

932) 1.Qxf8+! Kxf8 [1...Qxf8 2.Rxe8] **2.Rxe8+ Kf7 3.Rf8+ Kg6 4.Rxf4.**

933) 1.Qg8+ Kd6 2.Ba3+ Kc6 3.Qa8+ wins the Black Queen.

934) 1.Rac1! Ncd7 [on 1...Nbd7 2.Nxd7 Nxd7 3.Rc8+ Kf7 4.Rxh8] **2.Rc8+ Kf7 3.Rxh8 Nxb6 4.Rxb8** wins.

935) 1...Re5+ 2.Kc4 [2.Kc6 Bd7#] **2...Be2+ 3.Kc3 Bxb5** wins a piece.

936) 1.Qh7+ Qe7 2.Bf8! Qxh7 3.Rxh7+ winning material.

937) 1.Ra1+ Kb8 2.Ra8+ Kc7 3.Ra7+.

938) 1.Ba3 Nf6 2.Ne7+! Qxe7 3.Bxd6 wins the exchange.

939) 1.Qg6+ Ke7 2.Rxc7+ Qxc7 3.Qg7+ Kd6 4.Bf4+.

940) 1.Rxe5 dxe5 2.Rd1+.

941) 1.Rh8 Rxa7 2.Rh7+ wins the Rook.

942) 1...Qa2! [threatening 2...Qa1#] **2.c3 Bf3** winning the exchange.

943) 1.Qe8+ Kg5 2.f4+ Kf6 [if 2...Kg4 then 3.Qe2#] **3.Qh8+** winning Black's Queen.

944) 1.Ne5+ Ke6 2.Qg8+.

945) 1...Nxc4 2.Qxc4 Be6 wins the exchange.

946) 1...Qxf1+ 2.Kxf1 Rd1+ 3.Ke2 Re1+ picks up the Re6.

947) 1...Bg4 2.Qd2 Bxd1.

948) 1.Rxh7+! Kxh7 2.Qe7+ Kg6 [or 2...Kh6 3.Rh8+] **3.Rg8+ Kf5 4.Rxg5+!**
Kxg5 [if 4...fxg5 then 5.Qd7+ wins Black's Queen] **5.Qg7+ Kf5 6.Qd7+** and
wins the Queen.

949) 1...Rxd4! 2.cxd4 Bxd4+ 3.Kf1 [3.Qxd4 Nxf3+] **3...Qxg2+! 4.Kxg2**
Bh3#.

950) 1...Ndxc5! 2.dxc5 Bxc5+ 3.Kh1 Nxg3+ 4.hxg3 Qh5+ 5.Bh3 Qxh3#.

951) 1...Ra4+! 2.bxa4 b4#.

952) 1.Nh6+! Kh8 [1...gxh6 2.Bxh6! Qxh6 3.Qxf7+ Kh8 4.Qxe8+] **2.Nxf7+**
Kg8 3.Qg3! Qe7 4.Nh6+ Kh8 5.Rf7 wins.

953) 1...Ng4! 2.Bxd8 Bxf2+ 3.Rxf2 gxf2+ 4.Kf1 Rh1+ 5.Ke2 Rxd1 6.Nfd2
Nd4+! 7.Kxd1 Ne3+ 8.Kc1 Ne2#.

954) 1.Bh6+! Kxh6 2.Rxh4+ Kg7 3.Rah1 Rh8 4.Rxh8 wins.

955) 1...Rh1+! 2.Kxh1 exf2 threatening both **3...fxe1=Q+ and 3...Rh8#.**

956) 1...Ba6! 2.Qxa6 Qd2 3.Ne2 Qe3+ 4.Kh1 Qf3+ 5.Bg2 Nef2+ 6.Kg1
Nh3+ 7.Bxh3 Qf2+ 8.Kh1 Qxh2#.

957) 1...Bxg3! 2.Qxe8+ [2.Rxf6 Rd1+ mates] **2...Kh7!!** winning White's
Queen, e.g., 3.Rcc1 Qh4 4.h3 Rxe8.

958) 1.Bxf7+! Kxf7 2.Ne6! Nde5 [2...Kxe6 3.Qd5+ Kf6 4.Qf5#] **3.Nxd8.**

959) 1...Bd3! 2.Bxd3 [2.Rd1 Qf2+ 3.Kh1 Bxf1] **2...Qe3+ 3.Kh1** [3.Kf1 Nh2#]
3...Qe1 mates.

960) 1.Ke3! [controlling e4] **1...h5 2.Ne4+ Kf5 3.Nh4#.**

961) 1...Nf3+! 2.Kc1 Qg5+ 3.Kb1 Nd2+ 4.Kc1 Nb3+-+ 5.Kb1 Qc1+! 6.Rxc1 Nd2#.

962) 1.Nd7+ Kc8 2.Nb6+-+ Kb8 3.Qb8+! Rxc8 4.Nd7#.

963) 1...Rc1+! 2.Kxc1 Re1+! 3.Nxe1 Qxe1#.

964) 1.Rc7! Raa8 [1...Rxc7 2.Rb8 and Rf8#] **2.Rbc3! Rxc7 3.Nxc7 Ra1 4.Ne6 and 5.Rc8 and Rf8#.**

965) 1.Nb5! axb5 2.Nd6+ Qxd6 [on 2...Ke7 3.Rxf7+! Nxf7 4.Qxf7+ Kd8 5.Qe8#] **3.Rxd6** wins.

966) 1.Rc8+! Bxc8 [1...Kf7 2.Qc7+ wins] **2.Qe8+ Rf8 3.Rxg7+! Kxg7** [3...Kh8 4.Rh7+ Kg8 5.Qg6#] **4.Qg6+ Kh8 5.Qh7#.**

967) 1...Na4! 2.bxa4 [2.Kxa4 Ra1#] **2...Rxb6.**

968) 1.e4! [threat: 2.Bh6 Bxh6 3.Qh8#] **1...Bxe5 2.Bh6+ Ke8 3.dxe5 Qxe5 4.Qg8+ Kd7 5.Rd1+** winning.

969) 1.Bb5! Qxb5 2.Rxh7+! Kxh7 3.Qh5+ Bh6 4.Qxh6#.

970) 1.Nf7! Kxf7 2.Qxe6+! Kg6 [2...Kxe6 3.Ng5#] **3.g4 Be4 4.Nh4#.**

971) 1.Nxc6! bxc6 2.Bxg7 Kxg7 3.Qxc6 Nc7 4.Rc1 Re7 5.Rc5 Qb6 [if 5...Qb4 then 6.Qd6 Rd7 7.Qe5+ f6 8.Qxc7! wins] **6.Qxb6 axb6 7.Rxc7! Rxc7 8.Bxa8.**

972) 1.Rg6! fxg6 2.hxg6+ Rxg6 3.fxg6+ winning.

973) 1.Nxh7! Kxh7 2.Bxh6 g6 3.Qxg6+! fxg6 4.Bxf8#.

974) 1.Nb6!! Qxb6+ 2.Qd4+! Rxd4 [or 2...Qxd4+ 3.Nxd4 Rxd4 4.Bxg4) **3.Rxb6** winning material.

975) 1...Bg4 wins the piece since 2.Ng1 is met by 2...f3, and 2.Qd1 loses to 2...Nd4.

976) 1.Rd8+!! Kxd8 [1...Rxd8 2.Bxc5] **2.Nb7+ and 3.Nxc5** wins.

977) 1.Kd6!! d2 2.Kc7! d1=Q 3.Ra6+! bxa6 4.b6+ Ka8 5.b7+ Ka7 6.b8=Q#.

978) 1.Bxc6! Qxc6 2.Nd5 threatening 3.Nxe7#. Black has no satisfactory defense.

979) 1.Bh6+! Kxh6 2.Qd2+ and 3.Nxd8.

980) 1.Nxe6 fxe6 2.Rxe6+! Qxe6 3.Nxg7+ and 4.Nxe6.

981) 1.g4! Rh3+ 2.Kf4 Rh4 3.Rxf5! gxf5 4.Kxf5 followed by 5.g5+ and 6.Rxh7#.

982) 1.Nxd5! Ne8 [1...exd5 2.Qxf6! gxf6 3.Rg1+ Kh8 4.Bxf6#] **2.Nf6+! gxf6 3.Rg1+ Kh8 4.Qxf6+ Nxf6 5.Bxf6#.**

983) 1.Bb6! Bxb6 [on 1...e1=Q 2.Ba7#] **2.Kxb6 e1=Q 3.c7#.**

984) 1.Bxc6+! Kxc6 2.Qb7#.

985) 1.Rxe6! Kxe6 2.Qc6+ Bd6 3.Ng5+ wins the Rd5.

986) 1...g5! 2.Bg3 g4 3.Ng1 Bxg2.

987) 1.Qb5+! Nd7 [1...Qxb5 or 1...Nc6 are both met with 2.Nf6#] **2.Rfe1! Bb4 3.Nf6+–+ Kf8 4.Nxd7+ Rxd7 5.Qe5!** and wins.

988) 1.Nb6+! axb6 2.Qa8#.

989) 1...Nd5! 2.Qd6 [2.Qxe4 Nxc3+] **2...Nxc3+ 3.Kd2 e5** and the Queen is trapped.

990) 1.Rxf7! Kxf7 2.Rf1+ Kg7 3.Bh6+! Kxh6 4.Rf7 Qd8 5.Rxh7+! Kxh7 6.Qxg6#.

991) 1...Nh4! wins the Queen.

992) 1.Bg5 Bxf3 2.Qd2! Qxd4 3.Bb5+ and 4.Qxd4.

993) 1.Bxh7+! Nxh7 2.Ng6 wins the Queen.

994) 1.Rxb2! Qxb2 2.Nc3 followed by 3.Rb1 traps the Queen.

995) 1.Ne3 wins the Queen.

996) 1.Nf4 wins the Queen.

997) 1.Na4 and wins.

998) 1.Qf7+! Nxf7 2.exf7#.

999) 1...c5 2.Qe3 c4.

1000) 1.Nxe6! fxe6 [on 1...Qxe6 2.Rc8+! Bxc8 3.Qd8#, or 1...Bxe6 2.Qd8#] **2.Rc8+ Kf7** [again 2...Bxc8 3.Qd8+ wins - 3...Kf7 4.Qe7+ Kg6 5.Qxg7+ Kh5 6.g4#] **3.Rxh8 gxf6** [3...Kxf6 4.Qf3+ wins] **4.Qh5+ Ke7 5.Qc5+ Kf7 6.Rxh7+ Kg8 7.Qe7** wins.

1001) 1.Nxf7! Nf6 [1...Rxf7 2.Qg6] **2.Qxe6! Nxh7 3.Nd6+ Kd8 4.Ba5! Qxa5 5.Nb7+** and 6.Nxa5.

218

1002) 1.f6+ hxg4 2.Be6+ Ke8 3.f7#.

1003) 1.Ng5! [threatening 2.Nxf7 Kxf7 3.Nb6+] 1...Na5 2.Qh5! g6 3.Nf6+ Nxf6 4.Bxf7+ Ke7 5.Bc5+ wins.

1004) 1.Rad1 Bxg4 2.Rd3#.

1005) 1.Qh6+ Nxh6 2.Bxh6#.

1006) 1.Nf7! Kxf7 2.Rf1+ Ke8 3.Rxf8+! Kxf8 4.Qxe7+ Kg8 5.Qe6+ Kf8 6.Be7+ Ke8 7.Bf6+ Kf8 8.Qe7+ and 9.Qxg7#.

1007) 1.Bxf7+! Kxf7 2.Ng5+ Ke8 [2...Kf6 3.Qe6#] 3.Qe6 and 4.Qf7#.

1008) 1.Bg6+! Kf8 [1...hxg6 2.hxg6+ Kxg6 3.Qxe6+ Bf6 4.Rg3+ Kh7 5.Rxd5 wins] 2.Qxe6 hxg6 3.hxg6 and mate next.

1009) 1.Rxg6! fxg6 2.Qxe6 Rf8 3.Qxg6+ Kd7 4.Be6#.

1010) 1.Rxe8+! Kxe8 2.Qc8+ Ke7 3.Nxf5+ wins Black's Queen.

1011) 1...Qf1+! 2.Bg1 Qf3+!! 3.Bxf3 Bxf3#.

1012) 1.g4+ fxg4 2.hxg4+ Kh4 3.Qxh6+! Qxh6 4.Kh2! and 5.Bf2#.

1013) 1.Rxe6+! Kd7 [1...fxe6 2.Qg7+ wins] 2.Rxd6+ Kxd6 3.Nf5+ Ke6 4.Re3+ Kd7 5.Re7+ and mates.

1014) 1.Qxe4+! Nxe4 2.Bxf7#.

1015) 1.Rxf4! Qxf4 2.Bb4+ Ke8 3.Qxe6+! fxe6 4.Bg6#.

1016) 1.Qxd7+! Nxd7 2.Ne6#.

1017) 1.Rf7+! Kxf7 2.Qe6+ Kg7 [2...Kf8 3.Rf1+ and mates] **3.Qe7+ Kh6 4.Nf5#.**

1018) 1.Rxf6! Kxf6 [1...Qxf6 2.Bg5] **2.Bg5+ Kg7** [2...Ke5 3.Be7+ mates] **3.Qh6+ Kg8 4.Rf1 Rf8 6.Bf6 Qxf6 6.Rxf6** wins.

1019) 1...Nf4! [threatening 2...Nh3# and if 2.gxf4 Bxf4 3.Be3 Bxh2+! is decisive].

1020) 1.Bxh7+! Rxh7 [1...Kf8 2.Ng6+] **2.Rxh7 Kxh7 3.0-0-0 f5 4.Rh1+ Kg8 5.Rh8+! Kxh8 6.Ng6+** and 7.Nxe7.

1021) 1.Bb5! Qxb5 [1...c6 2.dxc6 bxc6 3.Bxc6 Qxc6 4.Rxe7+] **2.Qxf5 f6 3.Rae1! fxg5 4.Rxe7+ Kd8 5.Qxg5 Kc8 6.Qg4+ Kd8 7.a4!** and the Queen must give up d7 allowing mate.

1022) 1.Qg4+ Kd3 2.Qe2+ Kc2 3.d3+ Kxc1 4.0-0#.

1023) 1...g5 2.Bg3 h5 3.Nh2 h4 wins the Bg3.

1024) 1.Rxc5 Rxc5 2.Qd4 Qf8 3.Nf6+! Kh8 [if 3...gxf6 4.Qxf6 winning] **4.Qe4** and wins. [4...gxf6 5.Bxf6+ Kg8 5.Qg4+].

1025) 1.b4+ Kxb4 [1...Kb6 2.Rb7+ Ka6 3.Ra1#] **2.Rb7+ Kc3** [2...Kc5 3.Rb5#] **3.Ne4+ Kc2** [3...Kc4 4.Rd4#] **4.Rbb1!** and 5.Rdc1#.

1026) 1.Rxf6!! Bxf6 [1...Rxb7 2.Qg5! Bc5 3.Bf8! mates] **2.Qg5! Bf3+** [2...Bxg5 3.Bg7#] **3.Kg1! Rxb7 4.Qxf6+** wins.

1027) 1...Nxh3! 2.gxf3 [2.gxh3 Qxh3+ 3.Kg1 Rg3+ 4.Kf2 Rg2+ 5.Ke1 (or 5.Kf1) 5...Qh1#] **2...Nf2+ 3.Kg3 Qh3+! 4.Kf4** [4.Kxf2 Qh2+ wins White's Queen] **4...Qh2+ 5.Ke3 Ng4+! 6.Kd3** [6.fxg4 Qxc2] **6...Ne5+** and again the Queen goes.

1028) 1...Nf3+! 2.Kh1 [2.gxf3 Qg5+ 3.Kh1 Bxf3#] **2...Qh4 3.h3 Ne1!** threatening both 4...Qxh3+ and 5...Qxg2# as well as 4...Nxc2.

1029) 1.Rxb7 Kxb7 2.Qxc6+ Kc8 3.Qa6+ Kd7 4.Bc6#.

1030) 1...Rxb2+! 2.Kxb2 Qa3+ 3.Kb1 Rb8+ 4.Nb3 Rxb3+ 5.cxb3 Bf5+ wins.

1031) 1...Rxg2+! 2.Kxg2 Qh3+ 3.Kf2 Qh2+ 4.Kf3 Rf8+ 5.Qf7 Rxf7#.

1032) 1...Qxh4+ 2.Kg1 Qh1+ 3.Kf2 Qh2+ and 4...Qxc2.

1033) 1...Rh5! 2.h3 [after 2.g3 Qxg3] **2...Ng4! 3.fxg4 Rxh3+ 4.Kg1 Qh2+ 5.Kf1 Qh1+ 6.Kf2** [or 6.Ke2] **6...Qxg2#.**

1034) 1.Qg4! g6 2.Qd4 and mate at g7 or h8 next.

1035) 1...Bxf4+! 2.Qxf4 Rg3! 3.Qxf5 [if 3.Qxd6 then 3...Rxh3#] **3...Rg2+-+ 4.Kh1 Qh2#.**

1036) 1.c6! bxc6 2.Ba6+ Kd8 3.Qb8#.

1037) 1...Bxf3! 2.Qc3 [if 2.Nxe6 then 2...Rxh2+! 3.Kxh2 Qd2+ 4.Kh3 Qh6+ and mate next] **2...g5!** [threatening 3...g4 mate] **3.g4 gxf4! 4.g5** [4.Rc8 Bg2 mate] **4...Bb7! 5.Kg4** [5.Rxb7 Rd3+] **5...Qd5 6.Rxb7 Qf5+ 7.Kf3 Rd3+** wins.

1038) 1...Bxb2+! 2.Kxb2 Qxa3+ 2.Kb1 b3 3.c3 b2 5.Kc2 b1=Q+ 6.Rxb1 **Qa2+** and wins.

1039) 1...Qxh2+! 2.Kxh2 Rh6+ 3.Kg3 Ne2+ 4.Kg4 Rf4+ 5.Kg5 Rh2 [threat 6...h6#] **6.Qxf8+ Kxf8 7.Nf3 h6+ 8.Kg6 Kg8** [threatening 9...Rf6#] **9.Nxh2 Rf5! 10.exf5 Nf4#.**

1040) 1...Nf3+! 2.gxf3 [2.Kf1 Nxh2+] **2...Rg5+ 3.Kf1** [3.Kh1 Qh3] **Qh3+ 4.Ke2 Re5#.**

1041) 1.Nxg6! Kxg6 2.Bh5+! Kxh5 3.Ng3+ Kh4 4.Qe4+ and mate next.

1042) 1.Qh4! Re8 [1...hxg5 2.Nxg5 mates] **2.Bxh6!** gxh6 3.Qxh6 Ng6 **4.Ng5 Nf8 5.Re1 d5** [5...Ne6 6.Ne4! wins] **6.Bxe8 Qxe8 7.Re3 Be6 8.Nh7!** and Rg3+ wins.

1043) 1...Rxh3 2.Nf1 Rh1+! 3.Kxh1 Rh5+ 4.Kg1 Qh4 5.Ng3 Qh2+ 6.Kf1 Qh1+! 7.Nxh1 Rxh1#.

1044) 1...Be3+ 2.Rxe3 [2.Kh1 Rh2#] 2...Rd1+ 3.Re1 Rxe1#.

1045) 1.Qh5 h6 2.Qxg6 hxg5 3.Bxg5 Qe8 4.Bf6 and 5.Qxg7#.

1046) 1...Nf3+! 2.gxf3 Qh4 3.Rh1 Bxh3! 4.Bd2 Rf6 5.Rhg1 Bf1#.

1047) 1.Rxh6+! gxh6 2.Qxf6+ Kg8 3.Qxe7 Qc8 4.Ne5 threatening 5.Qf7+ Kh8 6.Ng6# while the Ba7 also hangs.

1048) 1.Nxg5! Bxf4 2.Qc3+ Rf8f6 3.Ne4+ Bxg3 4.Rxg3+ Kh8 [4...Kf8 5.Qb4+ wins] **5.Qxf6+ Rxf6 6.Rg8+! Kxg8 7.Nxf6+ Kf8 8.Nxh5.**

1049) 1.Rxf7! Kxf7 2.Qxh7+ Ke8 3.Bg5! and now 3...Bxg5 loses to 4.Bxg6+ and 5.Qf7#, while 3...Qc7 4.Bxg6+ Kd7 5.Bf5+ Ke8 6.Qg6+ Kf8 7.Bh6#.

1050) 1.Qxa6! bxa6 2.Rxb8+ Kxb8 3.Nc6+ Kc7 4.Nxe7 Bxe7 5.Bxh6.

1051) 1...Ne2+! 2.Rxe2 Rf1+! 3.Kxf1 Qh1+ 4.Kf2 Ng4#.

1052) 1.Qh8+ Kxe7 2.Re1+ Kd6 3.Qe5#.

1053) 1.Rxg7+! Kxg7 2.Nh5+ Kf8 [2...Kg6 3.Qe3! or 2...Kh8 3.Nxf6 Qe5 4.Bb2 Qxd4 5.Bxd4 wins] **3.Nxf6 Nxf6 4.Qxf6 Ke8 5.Bb5+ Kd8** [5...Rd7 6.Qh8+ Ke7 7.Bg5+ Kd6 8.Bf4+] **6.Qh8+ Kc7 7.Bf4+** wins.

1054) 1.Qa6 bxa6 2.Rb8#.

1055) 1.Rxh5+ gxh5 2.Ng5+ Kg8 3.Qh6 f6 4.Nxe6 Qh7 5.Qxh7+ Kxh7 6.Nxf8+ Rxf8 7.Rxf6 and wins.

1056) 1.Qxg6+! Kg8 [1...Kxg6 2.Bf5+ Kg5 3.h4#] 2.Bf5 threatening 3.Qh7# wins.

1057) 1.Nxg7! Kxg7 2.Qe5+ Kg8 [or 2...f6 3.Nxe6+ Kh8 3.Qg3 wins or if 2...Bf6 3.Nh5+ Kg6 4.Nxf6 Qxf6 5.Qg3+ Kh5 6.Qh3+ Qh4 7.g4+] 3.Nh5 f6 4.Qg3+ wins.

1058) 1.Rd7!! [But not the immediate 1.Qxh5? because of 1...Qxh2+! 2.Qxh2 Nxh2 3.Kxh2 Bxg5]Qxd7 2.Qxh5! gxh5 3.Bh7#.

1059) 1...Bxg3! 2.Bxg4 [2.fxg3 Qe3+ 3.Kh1 (forced) 3...Nf2+ wins the Queen] 2...Bxf2+! 3.Kxf2 Qxh4+ 4.Kf1 Bxg4 and wins.

1060) 1.Bxg6! fxg6 2.Qxg6 Nd7 3.Ng5 Qf6 4.Rh8+! Kxh8 5.Qh7#.

1061) 1.Qxh6! gxh6 2.Bh7#.

1062) 1...Qg1+! 2.Rxg1 Nf2#.

1063) 1.Nxb5! cxb5 2.Qc5 Nc6 3.Qd6+ Qc7 4.Ra8#.

1064) 1...Nf3+! 2.gxf3 Bxf3+ 3.Bg3 Qxg3+! 4.hxg3 Rxg3+ 5.Kh2 [if 5.Bg2 then 5...Rxg2+ 6.Kf1 Rh2 and 7...Rh1#] 5...Bxf2 6.Bh3 Rxh3+! 7.Kxh3 Rh8#.

1065) 1.Qxf6+! Kxf6 2.Be5#.

1066) 1.Rxg7+! Kxg7 [1...Kf8 2.Rg5 wins] 2.Qg3+ Kf7 3.Rh7+ Ke8 4.Qb8+ Kd7 5.Qxb7+ Kd8 6.Qxe7+ Kc8 7.Qc7#.

1067) 1.Bxh7+! Kxh7 2.Ng5+ Kg8 3.Qh5 Bxg5 4.hxg5 Kf8 5.Qh8+ Ke7 6.Ng6+! fxg6 7.Qxg7#.

1068) 1...Qf3+ 2.Bg3 g5! [threat: 3...Qf1#] 3.Rd2 [3.fxg6 e.p. Kg5! 4.Rd2 h5! 5.gxh5 Qf1+ 6.Rg2 Qf5#] 3...Qf1+ 4.Rg2 h5 5.gxh5 Qxf5#.

1069) 1. Rxh5! Rd7 [1...gxh5 2.Bh6+ Kh8 3.Qg5 mates or 1...Nxh5 2.Qxf7+ mates] 2.Rh8! [with the idea of 3.Bxf6+ followed by 4.Qh6#] Kxh8 3.Nxf7+ and 4.Nxd6.

1070) 1...Rb1+! 2.Rxb1 Qc3+ 3.Rb2 Qxb2#.

1071) 1.Qe8+ Kxg7 [1...Nxe8 2.Rg8#] 2.Qf7+ Kh8 3.Bh6 and 4.Qg7#.

1072) 1.Rxh7! Kxh7 2.Rh1+ Kg8 3.Rh8+ Kf7 4.Qf6+ Ke8 5.Rxf8+ Kd7 6.Qg7+ Bf7 7.Qxf7#.

1073) 1.Rxh7! Rxh7 2.Rxh7 Rf7 [2...Kxh7 3.Qh5+ mates] 3.Rh6 Nc4 4.Rxg6+ wins easily.

1074) 1...Nf3+! 2.gxf3 [2.Kh1 Rh5 3.h3 Bxh3 crashes through] 2...Rg5+ 3.Kh1 Qxf3#.

1075) 1.Rxg7! Kxg7 2.Be5+ Kh6 3.Nf7+ Kh5 4.Be2+ Kh4 5.Bg3+ Kh3 6.Ng5#.

1076) 1.Rxh7! Kxh7 2.Qf7+ Kh6 3.Bg7+ Kg5 4.f4+ Kh5 5.g3 [threat: 6.Ne5#] 5...Nh6 6.Ne5+! Nxf7 7.Be2+ Bg4 8.Bxg4#.

1077) 1.Qh6 and 2.Qg7#.

1078) 1.Rxh7+! Kxh7 2.Qh5+ Kg8 3.Bh6 Ne7 4.e6! Nxf5 5.Rg3+! Nxg3 6.Qg5+ and 7.Qg7#.

224

1079) 1.Nxf6! Bxf6 2.Qxh7+! Kxh7 3.Rh5#.

1080) 1.Rh7+! Kf8 [1...Kxh7 2.Qh4+ Kg7 3.Qh6#] **2.Qa8+ Nc8 3.Qxc8+** wins.

1081) 1.Bxh7+! Kxh7 2.Qh5+ Kg8 3.Qxf7+ Kh8 4.Nf6 wins.

1082) 1...Ng3+! 2.fxg3 Qf6+ 3.Qf2 Rxe1+ 4.Kxe1 Qxf2+ 5.Kxf2 c2 and wins.

1083) 1.Rxg7! Rxg7 2.Qxh6+ Rh7 3.Qxf8#.

1084) 1.Bxh7+! Kxh7 2.Rf7+ Kh6 [2...Kg8 3.Rg7+ Kf8 4.Qf1+ Ke8 5.Qf7+ mates] **3.Be3+! Rxe3** [3...Kh5 4.g4+ wins] **4.Qf6+** and mates shortly.

1085) 1.Nxg6! fxg6 2.Qxg6 e6 [2...Rf6 3.Rxf6 exf6 4.Bd5+ wins] **3.Be4! Rf5 4.Rxf5 exf5 5.Bd5+** wins.

1086) 1.Qg4+ Qg6 2.Ne7+ and 3.Nxg6.

1087) 1.Bxf5! Bf7 [1...gxf5 2.Qxf5+ Kh8 3.Ng6+ and 4.Nxe7] **2.Bxg6+ Bxg6 3.Nxg6!** and wins.

1088) 1.Rxh7! Kxh7 [1...Bxd4 2.Qxg6+ Bg7 3.Rh8+! Kxh8 4.Qh7# or 2...Rg7 3.Qe6+ mates] **2.Qxg6+ Kg8 3.Rh1!** and there is no defense against 4.Rh8+ and 5.Qh7#].

1089) 1.Rxg7+ Kf8 [1...Kh8 2.Rxh7+ Kg8 3.Rh8#] **2.Rg8+! Kxg8 3.Rg1+ Kf8 4.Bg7+! Kg8 5.Bf6+ Kf8 6.Rg8+! Kxg8 7.Qg2+ Kf8 8.Qg7#.**

1090) 1.Bc8! Rxc8 2.Ra8+! Kxa8 3.Qxc8+ Rb8 4.Qc6+ Rb7 5.Qa4+ Kb8 **6.Qe8+** and mate next.

1091) 1.h6+ Kg8 2.Qf6 and 3.Qg7#.

1092) 1...Nd7 2.Bxd4 exd4 and 3...Nb6# is unstoppable.

1093) 1.Qxf8+! Kxf8 2.e7#.

1094) 1.Bf6! h6 [1...gxf6 2.Rd3! Nxc4 3.Rh3 wins, while 1...Nxc4 fails after 2.Qg5 g6 3.Qh6] **2.Qg6!** and mate at g7.

1095) 1.Rh7+! Kxh7 2.Qxf7+ Kh8 3.Rh1+ mating.

1096) 1.Qxh5 Bxe4 [1...gxh5 2.Rg1+ Kh8 3.Bg7+ Kg8 4.Nf6#] **2.Bxe4! gxh5 3.Rg1+ Kh8 4.Bg7+ Kg8 5.Bf6+ Kf8 6.Rg2! Re7 7.Rag1 Ke8 8.Bc6+!** and mate next.

1097) 1. Nf5+! gxf5 [1...Kh8 2.Rxh7+ Kxh7 3.Qh1+ wins] **2.Rxh7+ Kxh7 3.Qh5+ Nh6** [3...Kg7 4.g6 mates] **4.Qxh6+ Kg8 5.Qg6+ Kh8 6.Be3** and 7.Rh1#.

1098) 1.Rxg6+! fxg6 [1...Kxg6 2.Qg3+ Kh6 3.Rf4] **2.Rf7+! Kxf7 3.Qxh7+ Ke6** [3...Kf8 4.Nf4 and 5.Nxg6+ wins] **4.Qxg6+ Ke5 5.Qg7+ Kxe4** [5...Ke6 6.Nf4#] **6.Nf6+** wins the Queen.

1099) 1.Qxh7+ Rxh7 2.Rg8#.

1100) 1.Rxe6! Nf6 [1...fxe6 2.Qxg6+ mates] **2.Ne5 c5 3.Bxh6+! Kxh6 4.Nxf7+ Rxf7 5.Qxg6#.**

1101) 1.Rxh7+! Kxh7 2.Qh1+ Kg7 3.Bh6+ Kf6 4.Qh4+ Ke5 5.Qxd4+ Kf5 6.Qf4#.

1102) 1.Rxh7! Kxh7 2.Rh1+ Kg6 3:Qg4 Bd7 [3...f6 4.Qh5+ Kf5 5.Nd4+ mates soon] **4.f5+! Bxf5 5.Qh5#.**

1103) 1...Bb4+! 2.axb4 Qe3+ 3.Kc2 Nxb4#.

1104) 1.Rxf6! gxf6 2.Qg3+ Kh8 3.Be7! and 4.Bxf6 wins the house.

1105) 1.Ne6! Bxe6 2.Qh7+! Kxh7 3.Rh3#.

1106) 1.Nxf7! Rxf7 2.Qxg6+ Kf8 [2...Bg7 3.Qh7+ Kf8 4.Bxh6 Ne7 5.Qh8+ Ng8 6.Bh7 transposes into our main line] **3.Bxh6+ Bg7** [or if 3...Ng7, then 4.Qh7 Re7 5.Bg6 Rxe1+ 6.Rxe1 Ne7 7.Nxf6 is crushing] **4.Qh7 Ne7 5.Qh8+ Ng8 6.Bh7** wins.

1107) 1...Nd4+ 2.Ke3 Nef5#.

1108) 1.Qh6! Qxe1+ 2.Bf1 and mate at g7.

1109) 1.Bf4! Qh5 2.Nxa7+ Kd7 3.Bb5#.

1110) 1.Qxc6+! bxc6 2.Ba6#.

1111) 1.Nxh6! Rxh4+ [1...Nxh6 2.hxg5] **2.Qxh4! gxh4 3.Nxf7+ Kh7 4.Bd1!** and 5.Bc2 mate cannot be stopped.

1112) 1.Rxh7! Kxh7 2.Qh5+ Kg8 3.Bxg6 and wins quickly.

1113) 1.Bf6! Bxf6 2.e5! Nxd3 3.exf6 and 4.Qg7#.

1114) 1.Rxg7! Kxg7 2.Rg1+ Kh7 [2...Kh8 3.Nxf6 Bxf6 4.Ne4! Bxb2 5.Qxb2+ f6 6.Nxf6 is crushing] **3.Nxf6+ Bxf6 4.Be4+ Kh8 5.Qh5 Bg7 6.Rxg7! Kxg7 7.Nd5+** and mate after 7...f6 8.Qg6+ Kh8 9.Qh7.

1115) 1.Bh6 Be5 2.Nxe4! Bxf6 3.Nxf6+ Kh8 4.Bg7+ Kxg7 5.Nxe8+ and 6.Nxc7.

1116) 1.Rxh7+! Kxh7 2.Rxf7+ Rxf7 3.Qxg6+ Kh8 4.Qxf7 Ng7 5.e6 Rg8 6.Qh5#.

1117) 1.Bxf6! gxh4 2.Rxg7+ Kf8 3.Rh7 and 4.Rh8#.

1118) 1.Qxh5! gxh5 2.Bh7#.

1119) 1...Bxd3! 2.cxd3 Rxd3 3.Qg4 Rxd2+! 4.Kxd2 Bb4+ 5.Kc1 Re1+ 6.Qd1 Qc6+ and mate next.

1120) 1.Rxf6+! Ke8 [or 1...exf6 2.Qh7+ Kf8 (2...Ke6 3.Nf4#) 3.Qh8+ Ke7 4.Rh7+ mates soon] **2.Rf8+** wins the Black Queen.

1121) 1.Nxc5! bxc5 2.Rg8+ Ke7 3.Qxc5+ Kd7 4.Qc8+ Kd6 [4...Ke7 5.Re8+ Kd6 6.Re6#] **5.c5+ Ke7 6.Re8#.**

1122) 1.Nxd5! Qxd5 [on 1...cxd5 2.Qxh7+! Kxh7 3.Rh5+ Kg8 4.Rh8#, or 1...gxh5 2.Nxe7+ Kh8 3.Rxh5+ f6 4.Rxh7#] **2.Qh6! Bd8 3.Rxe8** and mates.

1123) 1...Na5! [with the idea of 1...Nc4#] **2.bxa5 Qc3+ 3.Ka4 Bd7#.**

1124) 1...Rxb5! 2.Qxd4 Rh5+! 3.Kxh5 Qh3+ 4.Kg5 h6+ 5.Kf4 g5+ 6.Ke5 Qe6#.

1125) 1.Qd6 Qd8 2.Rg8 Be8 3.Rxe8 Qxe8 4.Qc7#.

1126) 1.Rxd5+! cxd5 2.Nd3+! exd3 3.f4#.

1127) 1.Ne7! Qf6 [1...Bxe7 2.Rxd8+ and 3.Qf7#] **2.Nh7+! Rxh7 3.Qxg8#.**

1128) 1...h6! and White has no good moves: 2.g4 R(f5)f3 3.Bxf3 Rh2#, or 2.Rd1 Re2 wins the Queen. Also if 2.Bc1, then 2...Bxb1. Finally, if 2.Kh2, then 2...R(f5)f3 wins the Queen.

1129) 1...Ba6!! 2.Qf3 [2.Bxa6 Qf2 3.Rg1 Qh4+ 4.Kg2 Qg3+ 5.Kf1 Qf2#] **2...Bd3 3.a4 Be4 4.Qf1 Qb2!** and White cannot stop 5...Qb7 followed by 6...Qh7#.

1130) 1...Rg8! 2.Rg1 Rxg5! 3.Qxg5 [3.Rxg5 Qh1#] 3..Qd6+ 4.Rg3 hxg3+ winning.

1131) 1...Ke3! 2.Rxg5 Rd1+ 3.Rg1 Kf2! 4.Rxd1 Bg2#.

1132) 1...Bf4! [immobilizing the Knight] 2.Kb4 Kd5 3.Ka4 Kc4 and White's position crumbles.

1133) 1...Bc1+ 2.Kg4 h5+ 3.Kh4 Be3! forcing mate since if the Nf3 moves then 4...Bg5#, while 4.g4 allows 4...Bf2#.

1134) 1.Rh3+!! gxh3+ 2.Kf3 g4+ 3.Kf4 g3 4.hxg3#.

1135) 1.Rxf6 Rxf6 2.h4! h6 3.Kg2 g5 [trying to unpin with Kg6] 4.h5! and now after his pawn moves are exhausted, the Black King must move after which Bxf6 wins.

1136) 1.Qe7+ Qg5 [1...g5 2.Qe1+ Qg3+ 3.Qxg3#] 2.Qe4+ Qg4 3.Qe3! and now if 3...Qf5 4.Qg3#, or 3...Qg5 4.Qh3#, while 3...g5 fails to 4.Qe1+ Qg3+ 5.Qxg3#.

1137) 1.Rg5!! winning Black's Queen after all pawn moves are exhausted.

1138) 1.h4! After all pawn moves are tried, Black must play either Qe8 or Ke8 after which b5 wins the Nc6.

1139) 1.Rc7! Black's King cannot move [Rxe7] nor Knight [Rxc8] and after a few pawn moves a piece will be lost.

1140) 1...Ndf6! 2.Bxb7 [2.Bxc2 Qd5 3.f3 Qxd4+ wins] 2...Rxf2! 3.Rxf2 Qxd4 and wins.

1141) 1...Rxa2! 2.hxg6 [2.Kxa2 Qa7+ 3.Kb1 Ra8 4.c3 b3! and mates] 2...Rxb2+ 3.Kc1 Rxc2+! 4.Kxc2 [4.Kb1 Rb2+ 5.Kc1 Ne3+ 6.Kxb2 Qc2+ 7.Ka1 Ra8#] 4...Qf2+ 5.Kd3 Nb2#.

1142) 1...e2! 2.Rxe2 [2.Rf2 Bg3] 2...Rxe2 3.Qxe2 Nxd4 retaining an extra pawn.

1143) 1...Qxd1+!! 2.Qxd1 Bg4! 3.Qxd8+ [If the Queen moves, then 3...Rd1+] **3...Nxd8** with an extra piece.

1144) 1...Rb4!! 2.axb4 Qc4+ 3.Kd2 Qd3+ 4.Kc1 Qb1+ 5.Kd2 Qxb2+ mates.

1145) 1.Qf6 exf6 2.Rxe8#.

1146) 1.Re4+! Kf8 [1...Kxf7 2.Ne5+ wins the Queen while 1...Kd7 loses to 2.Qxg7] **2.Nxd6! Qxd6** [2...Qxc3 3.Re8+ mates] **3.Re8+! Rxe8 4.Qxg7+! Kxg7 5.fxe8=N+! Kf8 6.Nxd6** with a winning position.

1147) 1.Re8+ Bf8 [1...Kh7 2.Qd3+ wins] **2.Rxf8+! Kxf8 3.Nf5+ Kg8 4.Qf8+! Kxf8 5.Rd8#.**

1148) 1.Be3! Qxe3 2.Qg4+ Qe6 [2...Rd7 3.Rh8+ mates or 2...Nd7 3.Ra8#] **3.Qxe6+ fxe6 4.Rxc7#.**

1149) 1.Rxd7! Qxd7 2.Nb6! Rxc2 3.Nxd7 wins material.

1150) 1.Qa2+! Bxa2 2.Rb2+! Kxc1 3.Rxf2 wins.

1151) 1...Rxb3+! 2.Bxb3 Qd3+ winning. [if 3.Bc2 Qb5+, or 3.Rcc2 Qd1+].

1152) 1...Qxd5 and wins! [2.Bxd5 Bxd5 and mate on h1 is forced].

1153) 1.Bxg6!! and wins.

1154) 1...Nc3+ 2.Ka1 Kf7! 3.h7 Kg7 4.Bd3 b3! and wins. [4...cxd3 5.h8=Q+! Kxh8 stalemate].

230

ORDER FORM

HAYS PUBLISHING
P. O. BOX 797623
DALLAS, TEXAS 75379

Additional copies of *COMBINATION CHALLENGE!* are available direct from Hays Publishing @ $14.95 each. Shipping and handling for United States, Canada and Mexico add $3.50. Total $18.45. Other countries add $7.00 for shipping. Foreign total $21.95. All books sent priority mail. Payment in U.S. dollars only, please. Quantity discount rates to schools, chess clubs, prisons, private chess instructors. Please write to above address for information.

Also available from Hays Publishing: *MY SYSTEM - 21ST CENTURY EDITION* by Aron Nimzowitsch. Text portions of this classic are thoroughly edited for the modern reader. Chess notation converted to algebraic format. 419 Diagrams. $17.50. Shipping and handling for United States, Canada and Mexico add $3.50. Total $21.00. Other countries add $7.00. Foreign total $24.50.

TITLE(S)_____/_____

NAME_____

ADDRESS_____

CITY_____STATE_____ZIPCODE_____

AMOUNT ENCLOSED _____